Books by Ronald M. Deutsch

Is Europe Necessary?
The Nuts among the Berries
The Grass Lovers
The Key to Feminine Response in Marriage

the key

to feminine response in marriage

the key
to feminine
response
in marriage

Ronald M. Deutsch

Random House · *New York*

All case-study names used in this book are fictitious.

Manufactured in the United States of America

Typography and binding design by Mary M. Ahern

Illustrations by Phillip C. Johnson, Medical Illustrator

ACKNOWLEDGMENTS

The author wishes to express his gratitude to those who have reviewed one or more drafts of this book and who provided research guidance and facilities: Dr. Arnold H. Kegel, M.D., F.A.C.S., clinical professor of gynecology, University of Southern California School of Medicine; the late Dr. Robert Kimbrough, M.D., F.A.C.O.G.; Dr. J. P. Greenhill, M.D., F.A.C.O.G.; Dr. Paul Popenoe, director of the American Institute of Family Relations (and to others of his staff who helped so unselfishly, especially Dr. Mary Hungerford); Dr. Frank L. Lock, M.D., F.A.C.O.G. The author is most grateful to the University of Southern California for the use of its library facilities, both medical and general, and to the literally scores of physicians, anatomists, psychologists and physiologists who gave so many hours in interview. However, it should be made clear that the accuracy of what is here presented is the sole responsibility of the author.

R. M. D.

foreword

Dr. J. P. Greenhill is one of the world's foremost authorities on the diseases of women. A charter diplomate of the American Board of Obstetrics and Gynecology, he is a life fellow of the American College of Surgeons and a charter fellow of the American College of Obstetricians and Gynecologists and the International Fertility Society, a fellow of the American Academy of Psychosomatic Medicine, Chicago, and an honorary fellow of the International College of Surgeons. He is author of such standard medical texts as Obstetrics, Surgical Gynecology, *and* Obstetrics in General Practice, *as well as editor of the* Year Book of Obstetrics and Gynecology, *and is professor of gynecology at the Cook County Graduate School of Medicine, Chicago.*

————

In the last generation medicine has made great advances in its understanding of how the body functions in physical love. Yet precious little of this has reached the public.

Because of this lack, the very vast majority of married couples are, all unknowing, denied the sexual fulfillment possible for them. Millions of men and women have been needlessly condemned to complete sexual failure. In many cases, the marriage is blamed, and often destroyed. On the other hand, countless women turn the blame upon themselves, and falsely believing they are inadequate, suffer serious erosions of personality. Today we know that in all but a few cases these failures and denials can be remedied; and for the most part not by complex psychological means, but by simple physical ones.

For many years, as editor of the *Year Book of Obstetrics and Gynecology*, I have reviewed the reports of new and often revolutionary discoveries of sexual anatomy and function. Yet, as a doctor, I find that few of my patients have any inkling of this knowledge. The vast fund of information available to the public has remained tragically out of date. The resulting knowledge gap is akin to what we might find if the last popular report on physics had been issued in 1935 and had scarcely been revised since.

Because this book fills the gap, I commend it to you with the hope that it will be widely and carefully read by both men and women. Frank, clear and scientifically accurate, it replaces the modern myths and confusions about the sexual relationship with the newest medical understanding. For the general reader, this is the first updating of sexual information in decades, and it is the rare marriage which cannot profit thereby.

J. P. G.

contents

Contents

illustrations

1

the key

NOT long ago I was asked to do a magazine article on a subject which seemed very improbable indeed. Supposedly, a California physician had found that a simple exercise could relieve the plight of women who rarely or never achieved satisfaction in physical love. The discovery had been made twenty years before, yet the public and much of medicine were unaware of it.

Tactfully, I explained why this could not be. First, today no important medical discovery—and this would be important indeed—is ignored for a generation. Medical "secrets" are the stuff of quackery. Second, for generations the cause of female frigidity had been known to be emotional disturbance. Even the psychiatrists found such cases very difficult. One certainly couldn't hope to cure them by flexing a muscle. I suggested that the editor of the periodical drop the idea.

But he persisted. He asked that I at least check the story with some of the experts with whom I had worked in the past. Reluctantly, I agreed, hoping they would not think I believed so dubious a tale.

I decided to telephone the most reliable source I knew on the treatment of feminine medical problems, the late Dr. Robert Kimbrough, then director of the American College of Obstetricians and Gynecologists, the chief organization of doctors specializing in childbirth and the diseases of women.

To my astonishment, Dr. Kimbrough, after the usual demurrer that there were no panaceas in medicine, said the discovery was real. It was not as simple as I had heard it. But it had been reported in many texts and medical journals. For twenty years, this particular exercise has been recommended by a coterie of specialists, mainly for other than sexual complaints.

I asked why this was not better known, and Dr. Kimbrough said that there were huge gaps between discovery and application in sex matters. He added that this was probably the most important of a great many recent sexual discoveries which remained unknown to the public and even to the majority of doctors. He urged that the article would serve a useful purpose and that he would review it, which he later did, along with the first draft of this book.

Intrigued, I promptly telephoned the editor and swallowed a large slice of humble pie. We chatted for a moment as the implications of the story sank in. Both of us had worked extensively on medical articles, especially those of interest to women. We considered ourselves quite sophisticated about such things. Yet, how little we really knew.

As I began to research, I found out that even this discovery was only part of a larger story, one needing much longer and franker treatment than was possible within the narrow compass of a magazine article.

Particularly, the authoritative medical view of feminine sexual response was changing radically, and the implications seemed poignant indeed for most marriages. No longer could the "frigid" woman be seen as that pitiable rarity—the cold, brittle, unfeminine female. Instead, as defined by her usual failure to respond fully to physical love, she appeared to be the typical warm wife and mother—not a psychological oddity, but a feminine common-place—maturely making do with scraps of satisfaction and expression in love.

For the fact is that women who are sexually unfulfilled to some degree appear to make up a majority of American womankind. And the old idea that she is thus, by definition, psychoneurotic is fading. For it has now been widely demonstrated that the key to relieving such a woman is usually a true understanding of her body and her sexual role.

This is not to say that emotion cannot block sexual response. It can. And I have no intention in this book to convey a mechanistic view of love, which I abhor, or to challenge the emotional or spiritual bases of love, in which I believe.

Yet the act of love remains a physical act. As we shall see, most authorities agree that in most respects this act is not instinctive, but is learned. And we shall see that for most men and women, the understanding of the act persists as a mélange of myth, confusion and superstition. As a result, in a day of supposedly great sexual sophistication, only the unusual couple achieves anything like the fully satisfying expression possible for almost any good marriage.

Though science has learned much about the physical side of sex in the last two decades, little of this knowledge has been communicated. As sex researcher Dr. William Masters wrote recently in the *Journal of the American Medical Association*, in answer to the question of a doctor who asked help in treating an unresponsive wife:

"With any marital unit, one can anticipate that the couple has a vast amount of misinformation, misconception, and quite simply, inadequate knowledge of sexual physiology."

This may seem curious in a time when we are so open about

sex, when the subject is so frankly overworked and coldly ex-
ploited by commerce of every kind. Oddly, it seems to be only
the useful and accurate information which is excluded from the
torrent of sexual dialogue.

Comments Dr. Paul Popenoe, the pioneer of marriage counseling who directs the American Institute of Family Relations: "Un-
fortunately, much of the literature on this subject in popular
circulation, and sometimes pushed by high-pressure sales cam-
paigns through the mails, is obsolete, if not worse. Books are being offered as the 'verdict of modern science' on which the copy-
right expired long ago. Any publisher can therefore help himself
to them without paying royalty, and this makes their printing
commercially attractive . . . All these books were good in their
time, but there is no excuse for forcing on the public today books
that are a quarter of a century or even half a century out of date."

Indeed, many books about sex which are widely sold were
written in the 1920s and 1930s, before the main research in the
field began. The text most commonly recommended, I believe, to
those who ask doctors for sex information, and often used by
the doctor for his own information, is Dr. Theodoor H. Van de
Velde's *Ideal Marriage: Its Physiology and Technique.* It was
originally published in 1926.

Most of the newer books do use the same information, usually
adding hearsay, personal experience and the subjective impressions of a few clients or patients. Many are not very explicit
about crucial matters. Others are explicit enough, but in being
so they offer mainly novel variations of the jaded or exotic tricks
which will never overcome a basic failure.

One reason for the continuing acceptance of Van de Velde,
Stone, and other earlier authors, is the belief that there is little
new to say. In the popular mind, this impression is fostered by
the simple fact that the press does not publish sex discoveries as

it does those in heart disease or cancer. It may surprise some readers to learn that the average medical mind has the same impression. For until the last year or two, medical schools offered no sex education. The majority still provide little or none. This explains why most doctors dislike being asked questions about sex. They are not trained to answer them. And we shall see that most doctors prefer to avoid the subject.

Where, then, can people turn for accurate sex information? Though there is far more freedom of sex discussion between parents and children, men and women, what information have they to give one another?

Decades ago Havelock Ellis, one of the first to dare sex education, summed up the problem rather neatly: "Suppose that eating and drinking were never spoken of openly, save in veiled or poetic language, and that one never ate food publicly, because it was considered immoral and immodest to reveal the mysteries of that natural function. A considerable proportion of the community . . . would have so many problems to puzzle over: How often ought I to eat? Is it wrong to eat fruit, which I like? Ought I to eat grass, which I don't like? Instinct notwithstanding, we may be sure that only a small minority would succeed in eating reasonably and wholesomely. The sexual secrecy of life is even more dangerous."

Ellis could have written the same words yesterday. In fact, even as I began my research, doctors and other professionals, expressing much the same view, announced they were forming the Sex Information and Education Council of the United States.

To learn what facts were available, I interspersed readings from the bibliography I have listed with interviews with at least sixty authorities in gynecology, physiology, psychiatry and marriage counseling. I reviewed the past decade of the *Index Medicus*, which indexes all key medical journals' reports. The American Institute of Family Relations made available its experiences with thousands of sex problems in marriage. The resulting text was then submitted for review to a number of experts.

I hope this text thus distills the most important of the new and often surprising sexual knowledge; that it will help lift the veil of what Havelock Ellis called "the sexual secrecy of life" for some of the many whose fulfillment in marriage may depend upon it.

2

the failure of
physical love

I N manner and appearance, Susan Cameron seemed far from being the classic portrait of a frigid woman. In her early thirties, she was attractive, warm and feminine and seemed basically content with her role as a wife and the mother of two sons.

"But Mike says I'm cold," she confided to a marriage counselor at the American Institute of Family Relations. "He talks as if I weren't normal. It isn't true. I've always wanted the physical closeness. Sometimes I begin it, and usually I'm deeply moved. But then, at the end, nothing happens. It never has."

It was not this failure which had brought Susan Cameron to the Institute. Most marriage counselors agree that sexual difficulty is rarely the presenting complaint, though it emerges almost always once counseling has begun.

Susan's attitude toward her failure to respond was also typical. She had not sought sex counseling—not only because of embarrassment or reluctance to appear inadequate, but because she tended to accept as normal the fact that most men regularly reach satisfaction and few women do. She regarded this situation—with some resentment—as part of the basic difference between male and female.

For many women this difference is a galling source of cynicism about their marriages, their husbands and their roles as females. When marital trouble arises, this resentment often becomes a bar to compromise and understanding.

Susan's first complaint was of violent quarrels which had ended in constant hostility. The battles had begun about money. They were building a house, and Mike—always a little too open-handed—wanted a showplace. Susan disliked display and tended to be tight-fisted.

Both Susan and Mike had been surprised by what an upwelling of anger seemed to be released by these quarrels. And both commented on the fact that one incident surfaced repeatedly as they fought—the fact that ten years before, they had been hurried into marriage by pregnancy. They had planned to marry in any case, they said, so neither had felt trapped or resentful.

But as the counselor persuaded them to talk about sex, he guessed why the unwanted pregnancy had become a long-hidden nettle, a symbol of their differences. For the drive which had pushed them into marriage had been frustrated. Instead of satisfaction, it had brought conflict and disappointment.

Susan's failure made her doubt her femininity, and she relieved some of this feeling by blaming Mike. "He's careless and clumsy," she said. "He takes me for granted and rushes things. I keep wondering what it might be like if he knew more, or did more."

Susan had other doubts. "I feel so deeply," she said, "that I know it couldn't be all my fault. I keep thinking maybe Mike was wrong for me that way, that it might have been different with another man. I feel strongly about adultery, but I admit I've daydreamed about it. I feel like a woman, and I want to prove it to myself."

For Mike, the failure was almost as damaging. "Susan makes

me feel so selfish. But I want her to share this. I read books, which give me the impression that I just need to go through the right motions, and Susan will be all right. I've tried some pretty ludicrous things, but it's always the same. Susan seems to respond to me—until the last. I end by feeling that I just don't know the right technique.

"And I have a sense of guilt. Susan has said she wonders how it might have been with another man, and I get furious. But in truth, I wonder if she's right. I have to admit that I wonder how I would have been with another woman—if I could have pleased her more, if I could have felt more like a man."

Carefully, the counselor explored Susan's past for the traditional psychiatric causes of frigidity. But he found little. Her family relationships in childhood had been good. Her parents had been openly affectionate and happy. She had never experienced sexual trauma or molestation. Pretty and popular as an adolescent, she had been interested in boys and sought after by them. She and Mike had been much in love through a long courtship, and she had wanted their weekends together before marriage as much as he. She wanted to keep her marriage.

The counselor had two conventional therapeutic choices. He could try to patch the marriage—both were eager to compromise—without securing good sex adjustment. But he had seen this approach fail repeatedly, as the sex problem remained just beneath the surface, ready to enlarge any trouble which arose. Or he could advise Susan to accept long-term psychiatric treatment, in which her personality would be probed deeply for some concealed block to satisfaction. But the counselor felt this long and costly process was likely to be unrewarding. Susan's psychological tests revealed a basically normal personality. Psychotherapy might do more harm than good.

But in recent years a third course had opened. The counselor referred Susan to medical help.

In his examination, Dr. Arnold Kegel—emeritus professor of gynecology at the University of Southern California School of Medicine and director of the small Kegel Clinic at Los Angeles County–USC Medical Center—made two basic findings. First, in interview, he learned that Susan, like a vast majority of American women, was unaware of just how her body functioned in the sexual role. Then, in physical examination, he found an inadequacy believed present to some extent in perhaps two-thirds of American women.

Dr. Kegel explained some of the newer information about sex to Susan. Then he explained the physical inadequacy, told her it was correctable, and taught her a simple exercise she was to do daily for some weeks.

Two months later, Susan Cameron had left the bitter ranks of what are unfairly called the "frigid" women. The closeness she gained with her husband and the confidence both gained in themselves and one another helped close their counseling case soon after.

Can such exercise and information really relieve this sad failure, which experts say mars most marriages to some degree? Even Dr. Kegel at first balked at the possibility. But today widespread reports confirm that, while obviously this approach cannot solve all sexual problems, it can and does succeed.

Dr. Paul Popenoe of the American Institute of Family Relations reports that, in a series of over a thousand cases of "frigidity" which received such help, some 65 percent of sexually unsatisfied women gained relief. Among the 35 percent who were not helped, there were deep-rooted emotional problems and a few cases of serious physical disease.

Consider, moreover, that the women in this caseload had marriages in enough trouble to require professional help. Such a group obviously includes far more disturbed personalities than one would expect in the general population, and therefore an atypical proportion of sex problems amenable only to psychiatric treatment. In an average population, Dr. Popenoe believes, the number of women who cannot be helped as Susan was helped is small.

"It is a rare woman," says Dr. Popenoe, "who cannot heighten her sexual adequacy through this understanding and technique, usually to a considerable extent. We now try to give the information to every woman we see professionally. We believe that this is a key to good sexual adjustment."

The Kegel exercises, as much of the medical world now knows the physical technique, are referred to in virtually every new medical text which deals with disorders of women. For their value is more than sexual. Their use is considered desirable in the management of pregnancy and childbirth, and is considered the accepted manner of treatment of some common disorders of women. After pointing out their use in the enhancement of physical love and the relief of unresponsiveness, Dr. Donald Hastings, chairman of the Department of Psychiatry and Neurology at the University of Minnesota School of Medicine, reports:

"Conditioning of these muscles is felt to be a valuable means in preventing undue sagging of the structures (bladder, vagina, rectum) supported by the muscles. Yet the simple exercises to accomplish this end are almost entirely neglected by American women; few have ever heard that such training is possible."

Says Dr. J. P. Greenhill, professor of gynecology at Chicago's Cook County School of Medicine, and editor of the *Yearbook of Obstetrics and Gynecology*: "In all the reports on the use of the Kegel technique there has never been any question of its safety for any woman. And for surprising numbers of women, its benefits, both sexually and medically, are likely to be great indeed."

How many women are in need of sexual improvement? And who among these can be helped by Kegel's work and other physical methods? Before we look in detail at these methods, let us consider how medicine has now changed its view of the woman who does not respond fully and dependably, of who she is, and why she fails and what kind of help she needs.

3

the paradox

FOR several generations, doctors have spoken of the woman who does not find full satisfaction in love as "frigid." The word bears a sting, and one which, for the vast majority of women so labeled, is bitterly undeserved.

The traditional view, in both medical and lay minds, is summed up by one current medical dictionary in this way: "Frigidity. In the female, absence of sexual desire. Inability to have an orgasm."

Herein lies a sad paradox. For it is implied that, consciously or unconsciously, the woman who fails to have orgasm does not want it. Let us see how this concept developed, and why recent research rejects the idea for all but a minority of women thus categorized.

A century ago frigidity was of no concern to physicians, whose attitude was expressed by the distinguished Lord Acton: "The majority of women (happily for society) are not very much troubled with sexual feeling of any kind." Indeed, Acton's Continental colleagues, Fehling and Windschied, both wrote that they considered sexual response in a woman to be a sign of abnormality, if not of frank disease.

It was Freud and his confreres in Vienna who first confronted feminine sexuality in a scientific way. (Feminine sexual response had been a matter of poetic concern for many centuries, as exemplified by the enormous Oriental literature on the subject.) Freud had found a strong sexual element in neurosis and had noted how often emotional illness expressed itself in sexual symptoms. He began to form a theory of the personality developing around a core of sexuality. And thus he reasoned that full sexual response developed only when the personality matured fully.

Freud reasoned that when sexual response failed, it was because emotional development had been warped and become arrested, leaving the emotions fixed at an immature level. Thus, failure to respond fully was a symptom of imperfect development, and consequently, a sign of underlying emotional illness. In this system, psychoanalysis was the only therapy for a failure of sexual response. Such therapy was to ferret out the hidden emotional block, allow the personality to mature and so automatically produce sexual completion.

In practice, the approach met with varied success, according to the many histories reported by psychoanalysts. And it is important to note that in most such cases by far the presenting complaints were obvious neurotic or psychotic symptoms. The sexual failure was merely one component of a cluster.

Until very recently, most modern psychiatrists have continued to view the woman who does not achieve full response in intercourse as, by definition, a neurotic. As Dr. Marie N. Robinson wrote in 1959: "When all goes well in the development of the young girl, both her personality and her sexual passions will flower . . . But if, as so often happens, thwarting or blighting experiences take place, the development of her personality and sexuality will be frozen at their sources." She sums up, a few pages later: "To put it directly, frigidity is generally a product of neurosis."

Certainly, it is established that the phenomenon described by Dr. Robinson and so many others is real. But recent research has asked some important questions about this long-accepted concept. Is this the only way in which women fail sexually? If not, what proportion of women who fail are emotionally normal? And what are the other causes of the failure?

It has now been widely reported that many women who are quite normal psychologically nevertheless fail to reach full sexual completion. A typical report is made by Dr. Peter A. Martin, clinical professor of psychiatry at Wayne State University in Detroit: "When I started in psychiatry, I was taught that orgasm in the female is related to the psychosexual level of development. Thus, a mature, emotionally healthy woman who had achieved a genital level of development should have a vaginal orgasm . . . [but] I have seen the emotionally sickest of female patients report . . . several consecutive orgasms. Also I have seen women who were the epitome of emotional maturity in all other areas incapable of vaginal orgasm."

Reading back into the psychiatric literature, one finds that long ago some of the chief exponents of psychoanalysis had second thoughts as they treated unresponding women. One was the famed Dr. Wilhelm Stekel, an associate of Freud and Adler, who wrote volumes on sexual problems. By 1926 Stekel felt "frigidity" had to be viewed in three different forms. The first was "the absolutely frigid woman," who experienced no orgasm and felt no response to any level of physical affection. The second was "the relatively frigid woman," who felt a little more in both ways. And third was "the passionate-frigid woman, who in spite of great longing and keen forepleasure is unable to achieve orgasm." Of this last type, Stekel wrote, "This is the form most often seen by us as specialists."

For "the passionate-frigid woman," clearly a better concept

was needed. She wanted the physical relationship. She was moved by it. Only at the last was she thwarted. Was she also a neurotic?

Many psychiatrists have clung to elaborate proofs to contain such women in the old explanation. But by the end of his life, even Sigmund Freud seemed to feel there were important unknowns not covered by psychoanalytic theory, that perhaps full sexual response was not necessarily an automatic component of emotional health and maturity. In 1935 a Mrs. Springer of Vienna wrote to him about sexual problems, and he replied:

Dear Madam:

I think you are right that most men are egotistical and ignorant in their sexual life and don't care enough for the sexual satisfaction of the female. The main fault, however, is yet not on the side of the man. Much more it seems there is a neglect on the side of nature, which is interested only that the purpose of the sexual act is being attained, while it shows indifference as to whether the woman gets full satisfaction or not.

The reasons for this strange neglect, about which the female rightfully complains, are not yet recognized with certainty.

Yours very truly,

Freud

One factor which certainly led to some early questions about an unqualified view of "frigidity" as a neurotic symptom was the overwhelming number of women who seemed to suffer from it. This was one reason why Stekel, for example, began to look for sociologic and physical causes. He wrote long and ardently about social injustices to women which made them resent the feminine role and the masculine assumption of authority. And he began to study the work of Rohleder, a sexologist of the time, who advocated, among other things, premarital examinations of men and women to assess their physical compatibility.

The statistical studies of sexual response provided some interesting insights. Such studies evaluate sexual experience in terms of what seems to be the one dependable measure, the orgasm, or sexual climax.

This phenomenon takes place after sexual excitement has reached greater and greater intensity. Pulse rates and blood pressure rise to heights often akin to those of an athlete at peak performance. The skin flushes. A driving tension is created, not only of the emotions, but of the entire body, with muscular tightening that extends to the hands and feet and neck. Suddenly there is an explosive release in the form of a series of muscular contractions, beginning with internal muscles and ranging through the torso to the limbs. This is accompanied by an apex of feeling, and then a descent from excitement and tension to calm. Without this release, this orgasm, the sex act is not completed. (Later we will examine the phenomenon, and how it occurs, in the detailed light of many new discoveries.)

Perhaps the first important study of how commonly women reach orgasm was made at the turn of the century, by the noted gynecologist Dr. Robert L. Dickinson. Dr. Dickinson asked four hundred and forty-two of his patients if they experienced orgasm. One woman in four answered, "Never." Only two of each hundred answered, "Usually."

Between these two extremes, the answers were suggestive, but rather vague. Forty percent said they had the experience "rarely." And another 40 percent answered, "Yes," without stating the frequency. Of this last group, however, Dr. Dickinson believed that about one-third were not really achieving true orgasm in intercourse.

Three studies were made in Europe during the next few years. Otto Adler found that 30 to 40 percent of women had no orgasm and probably felt little sexual response or desire during actual sexual union. Guttceit said that 40 percent of women "felt nothing" during intercourse, "participating in the act without any pleasurable sensation during the friction of the sexual parts and without the suspicion of a climax on their part." And Debrunner reported, "Over 50 percent of our women in eastern Switzerland know nothing of the sexual libido," without specifying precisely what he meant.

Still later, in the United States, Dr. Carney Landis studied forty-four women. He found that only seventeen of them reported "satisfaction," though he did not specify what kind or how frequently.

Though these studies took place at different times, and in only a general way measured the same things, one may draw from them some rough conclusions about sexual response in the first few decades of the century. First, only a rather small minority of women appear to have reached orgasm dependably. Secondly, a much larger minority, a group ranging from one-fourth up to one-half of the women sampled, never reached orgasm at all. Finally, what was probably the largest group had experienced orgasm, but over a very wide range of dependability.

At the time of these studies, many authorities felt that among the causes of sexual failure were prudery, sexual covertness, lack of free discussion about sex, and the teaching that sex was dirty or evil, a wifely sacrifice to be endured. Today, much of this has changed.

Our society is now criticized for an overemphasis on sex. Frankness in films and books and plays crosses with regularity the old bounds of taste. Promiscuity is reported to be much greater. For example, the increase of high school marriages has been explosive. And research shows that 57 percent and more of these brides reach the altar pregnant.

One study of Air Force recruits has shown that in 41 percent of cases the first sexual experiences of these young men had been with "a casual friend." Observing the figures on the trend away from female virginity, Dr. Clellan S. Ford and Dr. Frank A. Beach of Yale found that if the pattern continued after the next decade or two the bride who came to marriage as a virgin would be a very great rarity. One might expect that in such a setting most women would be well informed about sex. One might also expect that the increase in premarital and extramarital sexual activity would be motivated partly by greater satisfaction.

But modern studies do not show great improvement in the dependability of feminine response. Kinsey's statistics in this regard are complex (and not very reliable, some observers believe, because they are based on small samples and possibly represent selected groups). Kinsey usually relates orgasm to such factors as age, length of marriage, educational level and other variables. But drawing some general averages, it appears that by the end of the first year of marriage, perhaps a little more than a third of women have rather dependable orgasm. By the tenth year of marriage, this percentage increases to no more than perhaps 40 percent.

In more direct studies, Dr. Paul Wallin and Dr. Alexander Clark concluded that probably no more than 15 percent of American women depend upon a fully satisfying sex life. And they find that a large minority of women still never have orgasm.

Apparently, most American women suffer from some degree of sexual failure. In 1950, Kroger and Freed estimated, in the *American Journal of Obstetrics and Gynecology*: "Gynecologists and psychiatrists especially are aware that perhaps 75 percent of all women derive little or no pleasure from the sexual act."

Do these figures imply that the vast majority of American women are neurotics or psychotics with sexual symptoms? Such a thesis seems difficult to accept. And an answer is suggested by the work of Wallin and Clark, who gave questionnaires to four hundred and seventeen women, most of whom had been married between seventeen and nineteen years. Nearly all had children and seemingly normal lives. Wallin and Clark wanted to know if these women, though they might not have dependable orgasm, nevertheless experienced other normal responses to lovemaking.

Of those women who said they *never* had orgasm, or did so only rarely, fully *half* reported enjoying sex relations either "much" or "very much."

Of the women who said they had "some" orgasms, fully two-thirds reported "much" or "very much" enjoyment. And when questioned about moderate degrees of pleasure, 70 percent of even the women who never had orgasm reported such pleasure.

Volumes have been written on the grim frustration and hostility of women who, having been aroused, always fail to reach climax. One would expect such women to have soured on sex. But at all levels of satisfaction, the test subjects said they now found sex relations, as opposed to the early days of marriage, "more exciting."

Wallin and Clark conclude: "The evidence of our study . . . sharply challenges the assumption that women cannot enjoy marital intercourse if they do not have orgasm."

This does not mean that women should resign themselves to sex without satisfying response. But such studies do reject the old idea of the "frigid" woman. Truly, most such women respond to physical affection warmly and normally. It is at the last moment that they are blocked from completion. For such women, the word frigid, with all its implications, seems cruel and unjust.

University of Kentucky psychiatrist Dr. Beverly T. Mead comments: "The armchair . . . theorist may argue that a women cannot be a good wife and mother and be frigid. [He uses the word in the sense of being unable to attain orgasm.] Clinical evidence is too often against him."

And Dr. Mead adds: "The majority . . . know exactly what they are missing, and although we refer to them as frigid, they are probably not frigid in the classic sense."

But if women are so often quite normal except for their failure in this one respect, what is wrong? Dr. Isadore Rubin, marriage counselor of Philadelphia, finds that 75 percent of couples who seek counseling on sexual failure fall into the "normal group." Their needs, he says, may be met by "reassurance and sex information."

Keeping in mind that "information" in this context may have a broad meaning, do most American women really lack the knowledge they need for sexual fulfillment? As we have seen, accurate and modern sex information is not easy to get.

Speaking of what ought to be the most reliable source of such information, namely, the doctor, Dr. George W. Corner, director emeritus of the Department of Embryology, Carnegie Institution of Washington, says the physician has not been interested in the problem. He cites as one reason, "an illogical reluctance to discuss or even consider such matters, resulting from inhibitions which affected our doctors . . . surviving from the age called 'Victorian.' Such prudery . . . did most assuredly keep medical men from discussing with their patients, and from studying, mental and behavioral anomalies that were oftentimes more injurious and distressing than physical lesions of the genital organs."

Among the foremost critics of this attitude among doctors is Dr. Harold I. Lief, of the University of Pennsylvania. Having studied medical students and their curricula, he said in 1964: "Is the physician well informed about sex . . . ? Categorically, no! In less than a handful of medical schools is there even an attempt to adequately instruct students." He added that five out of six medical students were "overcontrolled and sexually inhibited."

The result of this situation was, he said, that "Nearly every student has some anxiety when dealing with sexual material, especially in taking a history from a patient . . . The student may communicate his own embarrassment to the patient . . . and he may never obtain information vital to the understanding of the patient's complaints."

In another paper, to emphasize the paucity of sex knowledge among medical students, he told of two students, male and female, who had come to him, saying they were to be married and wanted to know how to perform the sex act. Evidently, they had almost no information.

Dr. Lief and others are winning their crusade for sex education in the medical schools. "Until recently," says Dr. Alfred Auerback of the University of California's San Francisco Medical Center, "hardly a medical school in the U.S. provided formal education about sexual adjustment." Now, he reports, "About half the medical schools in the country have begun courses in sex education for their students."

But the old attitudes and levels of information persist among the vast majority of physicians now practicing. "There is often implied by the doctor's behavior," writes Dr. Joshua Golden of UCLA, "an attitude of rejecting the patient, perhaps conveying to one already embarrassed that his concerns are evil, unacceptable, or otherwise beneath consideration."

Dr. Thomas Brem commented—as president of the American Board of Internal Medicine, which decides on the qualifications of the nation's most highly trained family physicians: "The truth is that a great many of us are still Victorian in our attitudes toward sex, embarrassed by patients' questions on the subject, and usually badly prepared to give the help that is asked."

Ironically, this information which is so little known and so hard to find is basically quite simple. But without it, the chances that a woman will achieve sexual satisfaction in marriage are poor. Lacking such information, innumerable women are condemned undeservedly to the label "frigid," or at least to a needless doubt of themselves, their husbands and their marriages.

4

---

women
and the
anatomy of love

ALMOST always, women who are being helped with sexual problems make the same remark—"For men, sex is such a simple thing!"

In terms of orgasm, this is true. And there is a reason. For as a biologist sees sex, there is one essential—that is, that the male deposit a fertilizing secretion within the female, so that it reaches the ovum, the reproductive cell she bears, and thus continue the race.

Two basic events are needed. First, the penis, the male organ which deposits the secretion, must change from its soft, flaccid normal state and become firm enough to press apart the wall of the vagina, the birth canal, thus entering the passage. With a properly stimulating sight, thought, sound, scent or touch, this erection can occur within as little as three seconds.

The way in which the penis becomes erect shows the pattern by which the sex organs of both men and women are prepared for intercourse. Though some small muscles are involved in raising and supporting the penis, the primary process is one of engorgement (see Figure 1). The sex organs are well supplied with large blood vessels. In fact, the bulk of the penis is made up of two large parallel tubes, the *corpora cavernosa*, or cavernous bodies.

Figure 1 · Cross section of shaft of penis, showing the structures which engorge to produce erection.

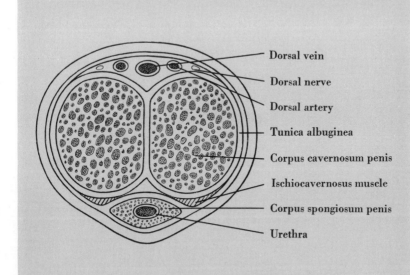

Dorsal vein

Dorsal nerve

Dorsal artery

Tunica albuginea

Corpus cavernosum penis

Ischiocavernosus muscle

Corpus spongiosum penis

Urethra

Just below and between these tubes is a smaller one, the *corpus spongiosum*, which carries the urethra, the passage through which both sexual secretions and urinary waste travel.

In excitement, blood flows into these three tubes of the penis at the usual or somewhat greater rate. But while the blood enters the structures rather rapidly, it cannot leave as quickly as before, so that considerable blood becomes trapped, making the organ swell.

Other sex organs also follow this process. The trapped blood causes enlargement and firmness, which mean greater sensitivity. For one thing, as skin stretches, more surface filled with nerve endings is exposed to stimulation. For another, the stiffened organs offer increased resistance to pressure, so that touch is felt more keenly.

If the first biological necessity is that the man quickly become able to have intercourse, to penetrate the woman, the second need is that he be stimulated until a reflex sends his fertilizing secretions into the woman. In order for this ejaculation of fluid to occur, there must be a series of sharp muscular contractions, which take place in the muscles at the base of the penis and in the surrounding area. These contractions put pressure on the vessels which carry the secretions, much in the manner of a squeeze on a rubber syringe, making the fluid spurt forward. This is the male orgasm.

In other words, to preserve the race the man *must* reach orgasm. (Some sperm can escape during excitement, but not enough, except in rare instances, for fertility.) The woman need not.

At most, the biological demand on the woman is that she respond enough to permit the penis to enter her. Thus, her orgasm becomes a subtler matter, something she must learn.

This view helps explain why science has known so little of female orgasm. For researchers usually tend first to problems of survival. Yet many researchers are becoming aware of another kind of survival—that of the personality assaulted by self-doubt, of the marriage threatened by doubts of love. In this view, and in our complex society, perhaps feminine sexual fulfillment is indeed a kind of biological need.

Today much more direct research has begun into the mysteries of sexuality. Among the best known of such studies is the work of Dr. William H. Masters and his associates at Washington University in St. Louis. Masters' work has been criticized on grounds of taste and morality, since it is based upon the observation of some six hundred and eighty-four couples, ranging from prostitutes to married partners in the act of intercourse and in other kinds of sexual stimulation, including the stimulation of women by a motorized plastic penis through which photos can be taken. His secrecy, in many ways understandable, has also brought some criticism concerning his adherence to scientific method.

Whatever the value of this criticism, one must recall the public outrage of centuries ago when the first anatomists began to dissect corpses to learn the secrets of the body. Many were forced to steal from the grave to continue their work. Without this work, medicine would still lie dormant in a thrall of superstition. Without sexual investigation, we shall remain sexually ignorant.

Using the work of Masters and others, some of whom researched decades ago but whose findings are still little known to the public, let us describe some of what is now known about the feminine sex organs. First, we might set aside one area of voluminous writing which overburdens most information about sex. For it is hard to find a "marriage manual" which does not dwell upon intricate systems of preparing a woman for intercourse through what is lamentably often called "foreplay."

The essence of reaching satisfaction, most such manuals conclude, is the husband's skill in preparatory manipulation, through stimulating what they call *erogenous zones,* or body areas which produce sexual readiness. This, of course, does not imply there are no erogenous zones. Nor does it mean to suggest there are no skills in preparatory lovemaking. But if we list all the erogenous zones referred to, all of the body is named.

Actually, this makes sense. For through learning, any part of the body can acquire sexual significance. From childhood, the personal experiences of the individual can give sexual meaning to almost any sensation, any touch, sound, sight, scent or taste. These then arouse in a very physical way.

But if certain body areas are really intrinsic to the chain of sexual response, they ought to be so for all humans, or at least all of one sex. Dr. Ford and Dr. Beach, studying a hundred and ninety cultures, found almost no such universality. Nor have other investigators. Even the kiss, in our culture basic to courtship, is not universal. In many societies, the kiss on the mouth is unknown. When seen in a film, for example, it can produce actual repugnance in the audience.

And what is stimulating in other cultures can be meaningless to us. A common expression of affection in other societies is sniffing the odor of the head or face. We understand this so little that we think the couple is rubbing noses. In one culture, the woman's pull at the man's hand is profoundly arousing to both, for here the gesture is a frank sexual invitation. In our world, hand-holding is innocuous indeed.

Even in the same society the same act can change meaning. Many manuals say the forehead is an erogenous zone. Yet, in another context, what seems more chaste than a kiss on the forehead?

What is paramount in preparation for intercourse is the individual's own pattern of sexual learning. In sexual matters, what is one woman's arousal may be another's boredom. This is part of what makes the love relationship so private a matter between two people who know one another well. What matters is that they express their affection in ways which are meaningful to the partner. To communicate, one must know the language of the recipient. In "foreplay," there is no system to know, only another person. Elaborate systems can introduce a self-defeating mechanical quality into physical love, and they seem to stem from efforts to work out paths to satisfaction without learning its physiology.

There are, however, a few body areas which seem to have intrinsic sexual value for nearly all women. Let us see how they function.

In the vast majority of women, stimulation of the breast produces sexual feeling and physical reaction. In a small minority of women—perhaps one or two percent—orgasm is reached by breast stimulation alone. (But some experts say this may be a matter of conditioning.)

The breasts follow the common pattern of engorgement (see Figure 2). Stimulation starts the trapping of circulating blood. This accumulates rather slowly. However, in women who have not suckled children, the breasts usually enlarge from 20 to 25 percent. Enlargement is usually much less in women who have suckled infants (probably because of blood-vessel changes which occur) and for women over fifty or sixty.

Enlargement, of course, makes the breasts more sensitive to pressure by exposing a greater area of nerve endings to stimulation. But before the whole breast becomes engorged, the nipple usually responds, aided by the contraction of muscle fibers within it. The nipple is so sensitive that it can become erect even through changes in temperature. The most sensitive portion of the breast,

Figure 2 · Typical breast engorgement in sexual stimulation. Nipple erection is partially concealed by engorged areola.

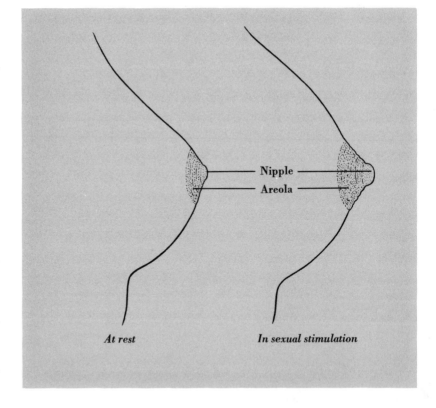

At rest   In sexual stimulation

it also enlarges proportionately more than the rest, lengthening as much as three-eighths of an inch. Very small or large nipples enlarge less.

More slowly, the areolae, the colored rings about the nipples, become puffy. They, too, are more sensitive than the bulk of the breast, and have one deceptive characteristic. Previously, some observers had thought the nipples lost some of their erection as emotion intensified. However, it is now known that what actually happens is that the areolae enlarge until they cover much of the erect nipple, making it appear to have become smaller.

This suggests another pattern of sexual stimulation in women. The nipples respond first and most keenly. But in most women, continued stimulation eventually produces only irritation. In a sense the nipples are *too* responsive. The swelling areolae help protect them. And because the areolae have swollen to firmness, when they are moved or touched the stimulation can be transmitted through them to the nipple, as through a moderating cushion. Thus, stimulation of the nipple may continue without irritation.

This and other phenomena imply it is a mistake to pursue relentlessly the stimulation of the very most sensitive areas of the woman's body. For it is as if her body presented highly responsive tissue to lead her into the experience. The body then appears to protect these most sensitive tissues. It does this by presenting secondary tissues as buffers, which are themselves responsive to stimulation but are less subject to irritation.

A more truly erogenous zone than the breasts is the vulva, the general name for the external sex organs of women (see Figure 3). These lie just below a bony prominence of the pelvis. This prominence is known as the mons. (The full name is mons veneris, or mount of Venus.)

The mons itself is not extremely sensitive. However, it does

Figure 3 · External female genitalia. The labia majora (major lips) have been partially removed.

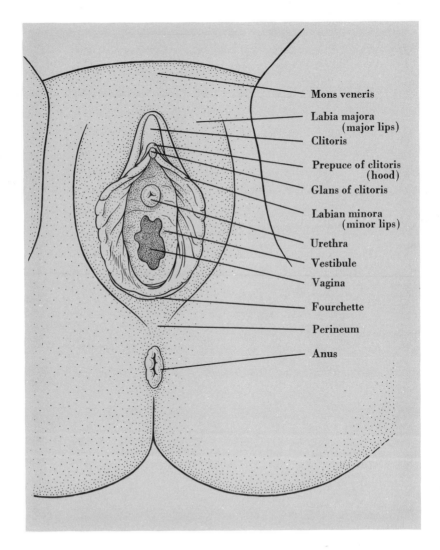

Mons veneris

Labia majora
(major lips)

Clitoris

Prepuce of clitoris
(hood)

Glans of clitoris

Labian minora
(minor lips)

Urethra

Vestibule

Vagina

Fourchette

Perineum

Anus

have a role in stimulation. For when pushed or pulled, it produces sensation in the more sensitive organs below it. Manipulation of the mons thus becomes an effective method of stimulation.

Below the mons, running backward between the legs, are two rounded folds of skin which join together like facing parentheses. These are the *labia majora,* or major lips. Of moderate sensitivity, they form the margins of the external sex organs.

From the topmost point at which the major lips meet, a raised shaft descends for about an inch or so. This is the clitoris, the organ which is the female parallel of the male penis.

The clitoris looks something like a raised tunnel, which widens as it descends from its origin at the upper meeting point of the major lips. At the mouth of this shaft there is a small rounded body, about the size of a pea. This is the glans of the clitoris, its most sensitive point, much as the nipple is the most sensitive part of the breast.

The clitoris has been a source of confusion in understanding how women fuction sexually. The most keenly sexual part of a woman's body, it was long taken as the seat of all sexual satisfaction. And because stimulation of the clitoris alone will produce an orgasm in nearly all women, it has been assumed that, whatever else happened in the sexual act, it was direct clitoral stimulation alone which produced the climax.

Most doctors thought the reason why a few women were regularly satisfied in love was a fortunate placement of the clitoris, so that it came in contact with the penis during intercourse. Size, too, was thought significant, for much the same reason. The result was that doctors actually performed surgery to expose the clitoris more, or to bring it closer to the vagina. Much of this confusion is now resolved.

Many women think themselves sexually inadequate because they have read that the clitoris becomes erect and they do not observe such erection in themselves. They look for signs of such erection in terms of increased size of the glans, the delicate little ending of the organ. But in a study of hundreds of women able to reach orgasm, more than half showed no enlargement of the glans at all. When the glans did enlarge, it did so late in excitement, and in many women such enlargement was barely discernible. In a very few the glans doubled in size. Yet it was clear that the size of the glans had nothing to do with satisfaction.

Some of this confusion about the clitoris stemmed from the common knowledge that the organ was the parallel of the penis. Erection of the clitoris was expected to be like that of the penis. It is not.

For one thing, most researchers agree that the clitoris, unlike any male organ, has only one purpose—sexual stimulation. But more important, from a practical point of view, when the clitoris has passed through its first phase of stimulation, it responds to greater stimulation by drawing up, not by extending outward (see Figure 4).

The anatomy of the clitoris does parallel that of the penis in one way. That is, it also encloses two cavernous bodies, tube-like, which will fill with blood. But when they fill, and the shaft of the clitoris enlarges, it pulls the supersensitive glans back under the hood of skin which covers the organ. Thus, in excitement, the clitoris is *less* exposed.

This is much like what happens to the nipple. A keenly sensitive body area is presented, leading the woman into sexual readiness, then it is protected to avoid irritation, while other areas receive the stimulation.

In size the glans of the clitoris is very variable. Of a hundred women, in sixteen it was about one-eighth of an inch high; in seventy-five one-eighth to one-fourth of an inch; and up to half an inch in the remainder. Masters, in another study, found the aver-

Figure 4 · Enlargement of clitoris during sexual stimulation, with retraction of the glans under the hood and away from the vagina (after Masters). Note how engorgement changes the relationships of all the structures.

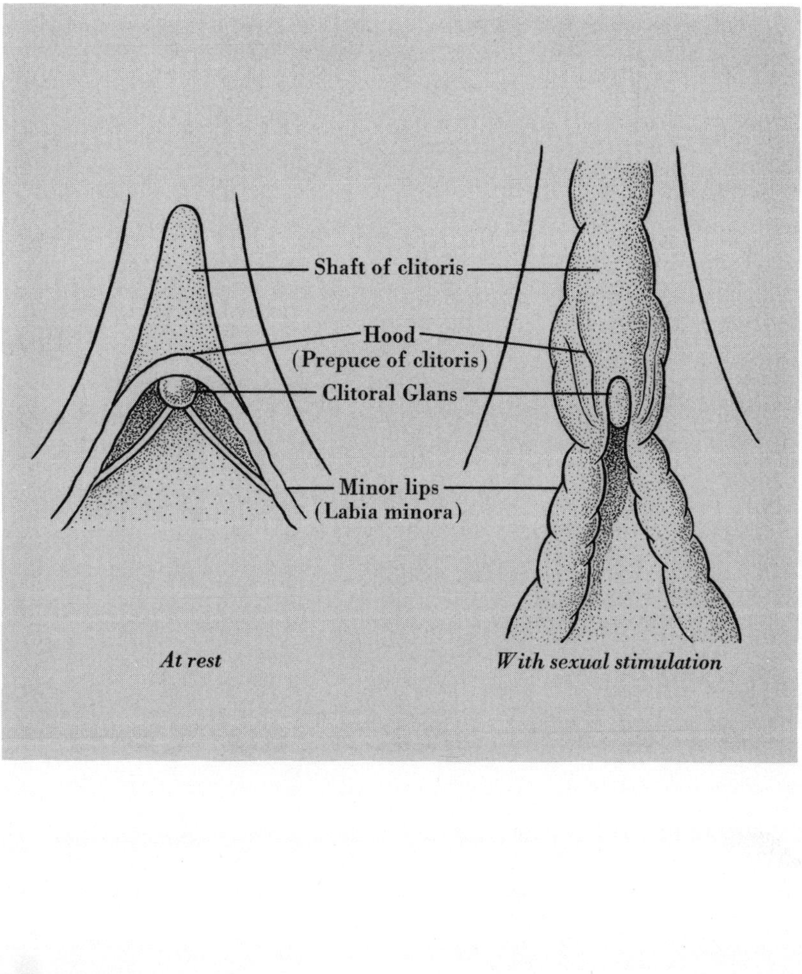

Shaft of clitoris

Hood
(Prepuce of clitoris)
Clitoral Glans

Minor lips
(Labia minora)

At rest   *With sexual stimulation*

age to be between one-eighth and one-fourth of an inch. Among normal women, he observed glans diameters up to fifty times as great as those of others. However, like others, he could see no relationship between the intensity or dependability of sexual response and the size of the clitoris or its glans.

Is orgasm possible without the direct stimulation of this unique organ? For decades the answer was thought by most to be negative. Clearly, there were two feminine sex organs of importance, the clitoris and the vagina, the birth canal. But if the clitoris was the source of feminine orgasm, doctors were hard put to explain the role of the vagina, except in reproduction. And it seemed unlikely that Nature would not somehow have contrived to make it most attractive for both sexes to seek the entrance of the penis into the vagina.

Most researchers finally concluded that the penis must be able to enter in such an attitude that it stimulated the clitoris. Many if not most men and women still believe this is the case. And this belief in the need for clitoral stimulation is the principal origin of the emphasis on contriving exactly the right position for intercourse.

But we have seen that this is not the fact, that the clitoris actually draws away from the vagina when a woman is sexually aroused. In observed intercourse, the clitoris is generally not directly contacted. Contact can be produced only by awkward effort, if not gymnastics.

Let us take a closer look at the structures which do receive more direct stimulation. The clitoris forms the apex of a second pair of facing parentheses, the *labia minora*, or minor lips. It is important to note that these lips connect to the hood of the clitoris.

The minor lips enclose the vestibule, the entrance to the vagina. Within this area lies the female urinary opening. The region is covered with a smooth, hairless skin, which looks different from

any other on the body. One reason is that this covering is con-
tinuous with the lining of the vagina itself. And functionally, this
area in many ways becomes one with the vagina.

With stimulation, the minor lips grow between two and three
times their normal thickness. The area they enclose also becomes
engorged. In effect, the lips brace themselves to the sides to help
support the entrance to the vagina. In fact, as they swell and
protrude, they add an extra inch and more to the length of the
vagina itself.

In this way, the minor lips also hold the male organ during
intercourse. And when the organ moves, it exerts some traction
on the lips. The lips being linked to the hood of the clitoris, this
traction in turn carries sensation to the clitoris.

The pattern of transmitted sensation holds throughout the area.
The chain extends all the way to the mons. Thus, stimulation may
be applied effectively anywhere along the chain. But with the
exception of the unique sensitivity of the glans of the clitoris, the
richest areas for stimulation seem to vary in all women. When
Masters studied techniques women use in self-stimulation, he observed that no two chose precisely the same approach.

It is clear how the external sex organs of women can be the
route to orgasm. But for generations the great puzzle of sex research has been: How does the vagina play its role? In fact, the
question has been: Does it play any physical role at all in bringing about orgasm?

The answers at first seem to be obvious. But let us look more
closely at this organ, to see why it has in many ways remained
an enigma to science, baffling efforts to understand women's response to intercourse, and leading many scientists to seek purely
emotional explanations for feminine satisfaction.

The vagina (the word is Latin for sheath) is a passage only
some three inches long at rest. The size of a woman has little effect

on vaginal size; in most women the length is remarkably similar.

Normally, the front and rear walls of the vagina remain in contact with one another (see Figure 5). But the canal is capable of tremendous distention to allow the passage of a baby from the womb. It is not surprising that any vagina can easily hold a male organ of any thickness, so ideas of sexual incompatibility being due to the smaller or larger width of the male organ are not accurate.

In excitement, not only do the minor lips extend the length of the vagina outward but the innermost end of the passage also enlarges by an inch or more. Thus, functionally, in intercourse the vagina is a total of perhaps five inches long. Again, these numbers bar male–female size as an important factor in sexual compatability. For the erect penis has been found to average between six and seven inches long, rarely very much larger or smaller. Thus, the very small penis is still longer than almost any mature vagina. In some positions, especially intercourse with the woman above the man, careless or very vigorous movement is likely to cause discomfort for the woman because the full penis is unlikely to be wholly contained by the vagina. With only the thoughtfulness necessary to any successful intercourse, relative size of the organs should not be important.

Engorgement does not appear to be the first response to sexual stimulation in women, as many people believe. The first reaction, the one analogous to that of erection in the male, is that the vagina becomes lubricated, to permit intercourse. Lubrication can occur in ten seconds.

Until recently, such lubrication was thought to come from either the cervix (the mouth of the womb, which enters the vagina from above at what is the innermost point of the passage when it is at rest) or from the glands of Bartholin, in the vestibule of the vagina.

Figure 5 · Cross section of the female pelvis, showing the vagina in a normal state.

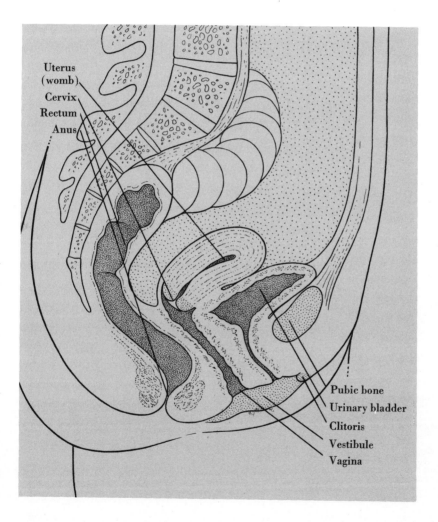

Uterus (womb)
Cervix
Rectum
Anus

Pubic bone
Urinary bladder
Clitoris
Vestibule
Vagina

Both these beliefs were wrong. The main source is a newly found "sweating phenomenon." Excitation causes the walls of the vagina to become dotted with beads of lubricant, much as moisture appears in beads on a cold glass brought into a warm room. So far, it is not known just what this secretion is and how and where it is made.

The walls of the vagina are covered with a delicate mucous membrane. They have many folds, or *rugae*. The walls are supported by muscle fibers, which surround the passage and run its length. And it is in these vaginal walls that researchers have hunted in vain for one perplexing factor—physiologists could find virtually no nerve endings in the vagina. This organ, though the woman's sexual center, appeared to be almost incapable of perceiving sensation.

As recently as 1962, Baruck and Miller described in *Sex and Marriage: New Understandings* the general scientific view that the walls of the vagina were "not endowed with sensitive nerve touch-spots . . . The vagina is made of the same kind of tissue the intestines are made of." They concluded that the vagina could not be the pathway to orgasm.

Small wonder that some experts explained feminine sexual satisfaction in terms of the mind alone, emphasizing "foreplay" as the carefully designed preparation for the moment of male entry, when physical stimulation had to shift to the purely psychological and yet somehow produce the very physical reactions of climax. Small wonder that they felt the correct attitudes, development, background and desires were the true sexual determinants of satisfaction. And it is not surprising that others concentrated their attention on contriving continued stimulation of the external organs, so obviously endowed with nerves, so quickly capable of producing reaction.

Was the clitoris really the only center of sexual stimulation responsive enough to yield orgasm? Dr. John W. Huffman, a gynecologist at Northwestern University School of Medicine, and others have interviewed women who underwent surgical removal of the clitoris because of disease. Those who had experienced orgasm in intercourse before the clitoris was removed continued to reach it.

(Huffman and other investigators also examined the theory that sex hormones were key factors in feminine orgasm and could explain the sexual failure of many. They interviewed women who had surgically lost all of the glandular tissue which produces such hormones. In Huffman's research, sixty-one of sixty-eight reported their sex lives were unchanged.)

Huffman concluded that his studies "would tend to bear out the assumption that the vagina becomes the center of normal sexual activity in the mature female."

Ford and Beach confirmed this in their study of many cultures. They found primitive groups in which the clitoris was removed in puberty rites. Still, the women reached full satisfaction.

This work seems to bear out the early idea that there might be two kinds of feminine orgasm. Certainly many women capable of climax through direct stimulation of the clitoris, as in petting or masturbation, failed to reach orgasm in intercourse.

Freud used this concept, reasoning that the clitoral orgasm was adolescent and a phase of development and that true maturity was reached when a woman could achieve orgasm in and through the vagina. This view is still held by many psychiatrists. Dr. Marie N. Robinson explains it: "The clitoral orgasm takes place on the clitoris only. It excludes the vagina from sensual participation and it is often independent of the male penis. This kind of orgasm is possible at any early state in female development."

Physically, however, doctors could find no sensory pathway in the vagina to serve as a mechanism for vaginal orgasm. Moreover, so far, the physical reactions of a woman's orgasm look much the same to observers whether it is induced externally or vaginally.

The concept of vaginal orgasm might have been abandoned entirely were it not for the insistence of women patients that they felt it, and that it was different somehow. "In discussions with thousands of women," says Dr. Paul Popenoe, "our counselors find the clitoral orgasm is described as superficial, a nervous contraction which is not fully satisfying. The vaginal orgasm is described as being profound, seeming to involve the entire body in an explosive warmth and providing a very rich and deep release and satisfaction. It is clear, however, that a very great many women have rarely or never experienced such a climax."

Dr. Philip Polatin, of Columbia University, writes: "A woman's sexual response differs from a man's because she has not one but two means of achieving orgasm, and these two kinds of orgasm differ markedly from each other. Also, both may occur simultaneously, or one may follow rapidly on the other. . . .

"First, there is what is known as the clitoral orgasm, induced by stimulation of the clitoris . . . Some women do not know any other type of orgasm . . . a prolonged nervous excitation resulting in a sharp climax. Then there is the vaginal orgasm, experienced deep within the vagina."

Certainly it is true that women capable of satisfaction are moved deeply by the entrance of the male organ, that they become deeply stimulated by intercourse itself and reach orgasm without, at times, much if any external stimulation. The sensations they describe feeling in intercourse are quite physical and quite real. Yet other women do not feel these sensations, or feel them only vaguely.

What do these sensations come from? Why do some women have them while others do not? How can there be sensations of any kind, if indeed the vagina differs little from a length of insensate intestine?

The new sex research appears to have unraveled much of this mystery. In doing so, it seems to have provided a key to a better physical understanding of sex, by means of which therapists are now able to guide women to full response with quite brief and simple counseling.

5

---

an

accidental answer

ARLY in the 1940's, a woman we shall call Doris Wilson became the mother of her third child. Until this time, Mrs. Wilson's health had been good. But after her third delivery she found herself distressed and embarrassed by a curious problem.

Her doctor called it urinary stress incontinence. He told Mrs. Wilson that as many as one of every twenty American women was similarly afflicted. A laugh, a cough, a sudden movement would cause the urinary bladder to release a little of its contents.

Doris Wilson had to wear a protective pad and be cautious when in public. The doctor prescribed drugs, but they did not help. After two years, Mrs. Wilson was desperate. Her doctor told her surgery might provide relief by adjusting the position of the bladder. But he cautioned that such surgery had an indifferent record of success and that it was not without hazards.

But Mrs. Wilson was determined to try. She was sent to a surgeon, Dr. Arnold H. Kegel, who specialized in disorders of women. Kegel had been keenly interested in stress incontinence and dissatisfied with the results of surgical treatment. For one thing the true cause of the problem was still unclear. Even when surgery succeeded, the relief might be only temporary. He sought a better answer.

He told Mrs. Wilson he suspected that a weakened muscle was at fault. This muscle ran between the legs, from front to back, like a sling. It was wide and strong. In fact, it formed the floor of the pelvis, the lower trunk. It was the base of support for the bladder, part of the rectum, the birth canal and the womb.

In women, three passages penetrated this muscle to empty outside the body—the rectum, birth canal and the urethra, or urinary canal. Kegel believed that, since the birth canal passed through the muscle and was firmly attached to it, childbirth could damage the muscle. And since the urinary passage was supported by the same muscle and kept closed by it, a weak muscle might mean poor urinary control. The muscle might be strong enough to hold back urine ordinarily. But with extra stress, some of the fluid would push through. Kegel also believed that this muscle might be strengthened.

Mrs. Wilson was one of several stress-incontinence patients who agreed to try special exercises. In less than two months, the distress and embarrassment had ended.

Today these exercises, known as the Kegel exercises, are standard technique in cases of stress incontinence. For most patients, they succeed and make surgery needless.

Shortly after Mrs. Wilson had gained urinary control, she confided to Dr. Kegel that something else had happened. For the first time in fifteen years of marriage, she had reached orgasm in intercourse. She wanted to know if this could be associated with the exercises.

Kegel was skeptical. But then he heard the same thing repeatedly from women given instructions for the exercises. He wondered about a possible mechanism.

To understand Kegel's reasoning, one must know something of the pelvic floor muscles. They are composed of several layers. The outermost layer is made up mainly of sphincters, ring-like

Figure 6· The three lower muscle diaphragms of the pelvic floor.

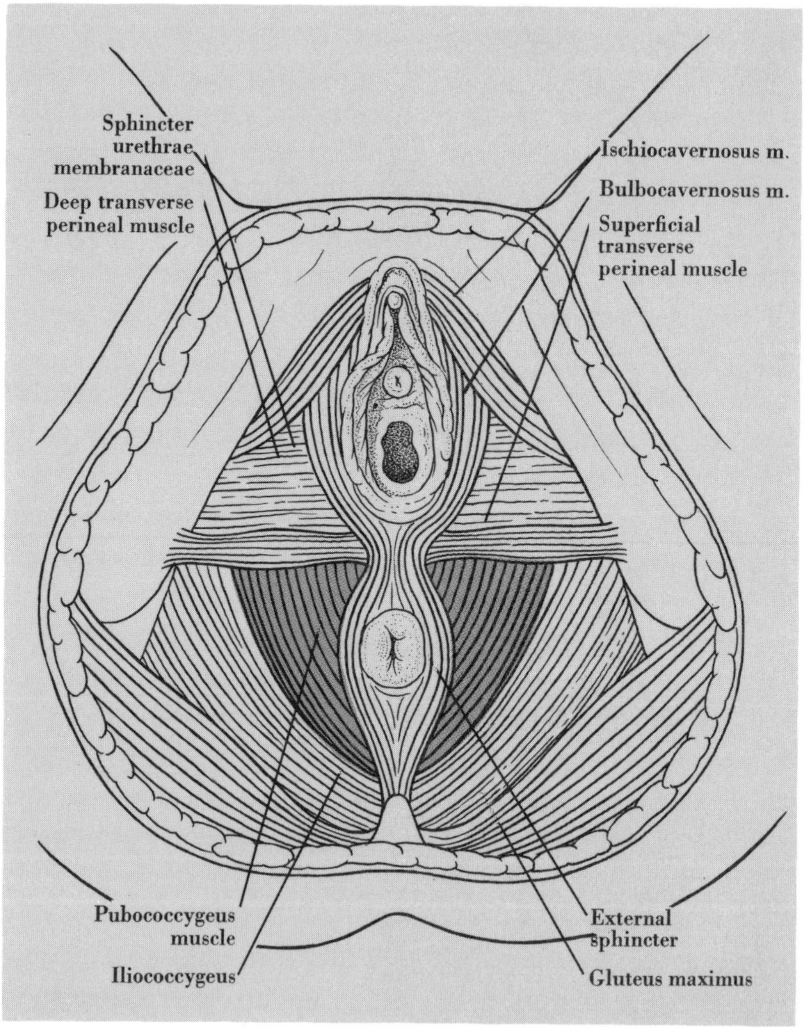

closing muscles. These muscles close the outer openings of the urinary passage, rectum and birth canal. They are relatively weak. For example, women with stress incontinence usually depend upon the more external urinary sphincter to close the urinary passage, a job it can do only imperfectly.

But lying inside these outer muscle layers is an extremely strong muscle, more than two fingers thick (see Figures 6–10). It is known as the *pubococcygeus* (pronounced pyoo'bo koksij'eus), for it runs from the pubis, the bony prominence at the front of the pelvis, to the coccyx, the end of the spine. (Some doctors use different names for this muscle, which is present in both men and women. In the past it has been commonly referred to as a portion of the *levator ani*, which is so called because it can lift the anus. In practical terms, the name used is not very important. As a convenience, we will use the name P.C.)

Picture the three canals passing through the muscular floor. Each passage is surrounded by a net of interlocking muscle fibers from the P.C., for a length up to about two inches. The fibers run both lengthwise along each canal and surround each as sphincters. Thus, the rings of muscle around each passage can be squeezed shut at will.

It is the sphincteric action of that part of the P.C. surrounding the urinary passage which fails in stress incontinence; the P.C. cannot squeeze the passage shut. Exercise gives it strength enough to function properly.

What has this to do with sexual satisfaction? Kegel knew that the P.C. surrounded the vagina in the same way. And he began to find that a surprising number of women had P.C. weakness.

In fewer than one of three women the muscle had relatively good tone, making a rather firm straight platform and performing well. Among these women, urinary incontinence was a rarity. (It should be added that the disorder can have causes other than

Figure 7· The pubococcygeus muscle after removal of the more superficial muscles. Note how the fibers surround the urinary passage, vagina and rectum, interlocking with other muscle fibers of these organs.

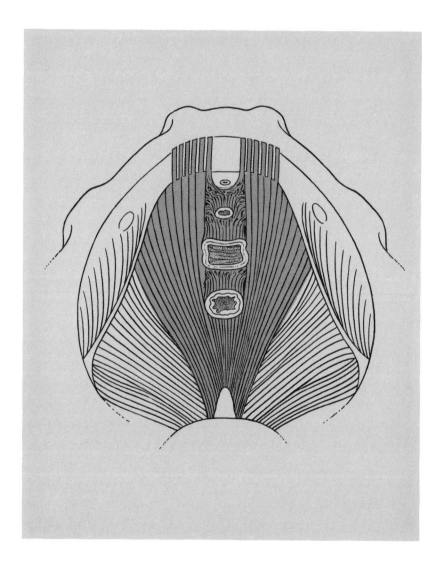

Figure 8· The pubococcygeus muscle, seen from above.

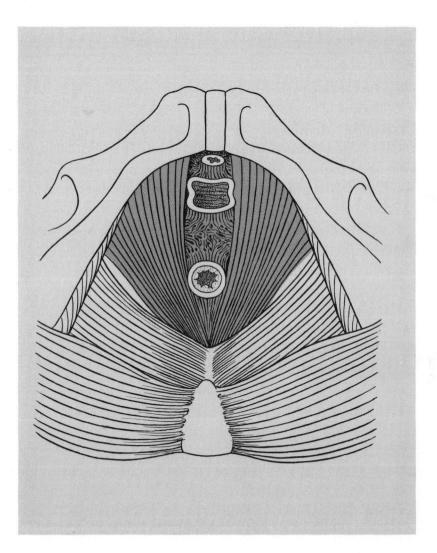

muscle failure.) Childbirth was easier for them. The birth canal seemed rarely to be damaged in delivery. And sexual responsiveness tended to be good.

But in at least two of three women the P.C. was relatively slack and weak. It sagged much like a hammock (see Figures 9 and 10); and organs sagged which it was meant to support. Among these women, childbirth was more likely to be difficult. Birth-canal injuries were more common. Incontinence appeared after children were born, and sometimes as early as their own childhoods. Sexual satisfaction was unusual.

Oddly, the strength of the P.C. seemed unrelated to the general muscular strength of the patient. Female athletes might have poor, slack P.C. musculature. Some frail, sedentary women had good tone. The explanation was that the P.C. was suspended between two fixed bony structures. Therefore, it was unaffected by the use of other muscles. It stood alone.

Gradually Kegel developed a way to exercise and strengthen the P.C. In 1947 the USC School of Medicine established a clinic in which he could continue his work, and in 1948 his work won the annual award of the Los Angeles Obstetrical Society.

Though Kegel's primary interest had not been in sexual problems, he felt obliged to pursue the sexual component of his findings. At his clinic, he began to accept referrals from the American Institute of Family Relations of women who failed sexually.

Recall the case of Susan Cameron, which we discussed earlier. She had been affectionate and found pleasure in physical love, but could not attain orgasm. In fact, she felt little physical stimulation once intercourse began. She had been psychologically normal.

When he had examined Mrs. Cameron, Dr. Kegel showed her two molds to demonstrate his findings. These molds, called *moulages* (see Figures 11–13), had been formed by inserting a special soft plastic material into the vagina. When the material had shaped itself to the organ, it was removed, making an almost perfect model of the vaginal passage.

One mold was made from the vagina of a woman with good P.C. muscle tone. It looked something like a squeezed tube. Wide at the opening, it narrowed for a space of about two inches, then widened again. The narrowing showed the squeezing action of a strong P.C. Throughout the narrowed portion, the mold rippled slightly, the ripples made by the pressure of tightening muscle bands, row on row. These bands were the spreading fibers of the P.C. They made the vagina a strong, muscular organ.

The second mold was made from the vagina of a patient who had never experienced true orgasm. It looked rather like a straight-sided funnel, broadening steadily from its opening toward the top. Its walls were virtually unmarked by muscle pressure. Clearly the P.C. was weak. The organ had poor support and little strength.

"The second mold," the doctor told Mrs. Cameron, "approximates your own condition. You can see that the vagina from which this mold was made cannot exert the pressure which is an essential for good sexual function."

Why is the ability to exert pressure important? The answer to this question explains to many experts the ancient puzzle of how the vagina can provide sexual satisfaction when it appears to contain almost no nerve endings.

The solution is explained this way by Dr. Terence F. McGuire and Dr. Richard M. Steinhilber of the Mayo Clinic: "According to current data, the muscles beneath the vaginal mucosa [the lining of the vagina] are well supplied with proprioceptive endings [nerve endings of the type sensitive to pressure, movement and stretching]. These are adequately stimulated during intercourse, and could well represent the primary . . . sensory ap-

Figure 9 · The pubococcygeus muscle with good tone and proper position.

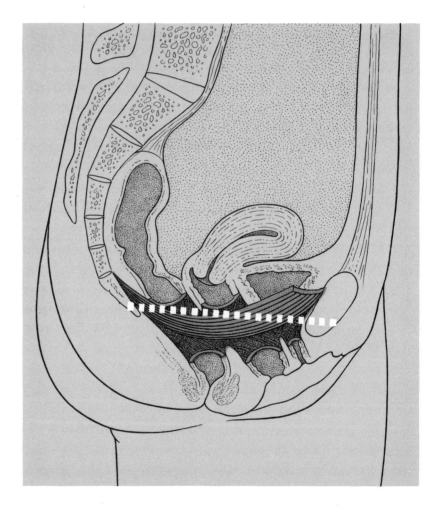

Figure 10 · The pubococcygeus muscle with poor tone and position. Note the sagging of structures due to weak support.

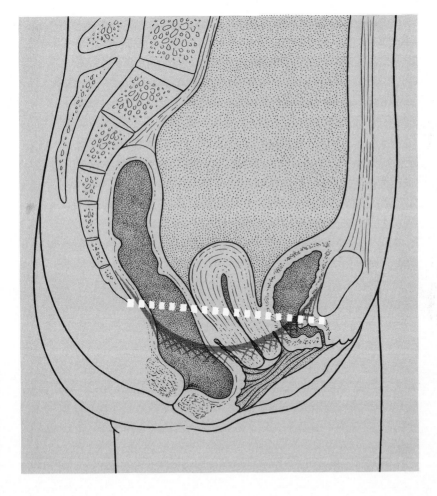

paratus . . . It would appear that vaginal orgasm is a reality."

In other words, the muscle which surrounds the vagina is rich in sensitive nerve endings. Doctors failed to find these endings because their search was limited to the lining of the vagina.

Since these nerves are outside the vagina, it takes firm pressure from within to stimulate them. In a wide, slack vagina, the male organ makes poor and infrequent contact with the walls of the passage, thereby stimulating nerves in the surrounding musculature very little.

If the vagina is narrowed to a tight, firm channel by the contraction of surrounding muscle, the male organ will press and push these muscles, giving strong stimulation (see Figure 14). Stimulated, the muscles will respond with an automatic contraction which increases the contact, thus helping to build the tension which leads to feminine climax.

This phenomenon had long been suspected by some observers. As early as the turn of the century, Dr. Robert L. Dickinson reported that he could identify women likely to fail sexually by examining them. He wrote: "The size, power, reactions and rhythm of contraction of the pelvic floor muscles give information concerning vaginal types of coital orgasm [orgasm during intercourse]."

In one of his early case records he noted: "Levator [one way of referring to this musculature] is not very good. Taught her to use the muscle." And he adds, "It seems very important that many women are able after instruction to get something which they call orgasm, when they failed before instruction."

Some primitive and Oriental peoples have observed the need for such muscular control and strength and teach young women accordingly. In one African tribe, no girl may marry until she is able to exert strong pressure with the vaginal muscles. Other cultures have noted that sexual performance is often poorer after

Figure 11 · (*Left*) A moulage of a vagina with good muscle tone, seen in the anterior (front) view. (*Right*) A moulage of a vagina with poor muscle tone, seen in the anterior (front) view. (*Photograph from Dr. Kegel's case files*)

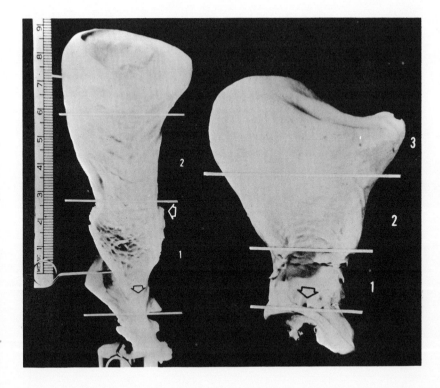

Figure 12 · Moulages of two vaginas, seen from the lateral (side) view, with the pubococcygeus muscle in a relaxed state. (*Top*) A moulage of a vagina with good muscle tone. The narrowing, produced by the muscle, is seen in the middle segment (2). (*Bottom*) A moulage of a vagina with poor muscle tone. (*Photograph from Dr. Kegel's case files*)

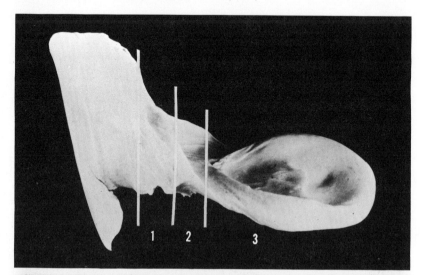

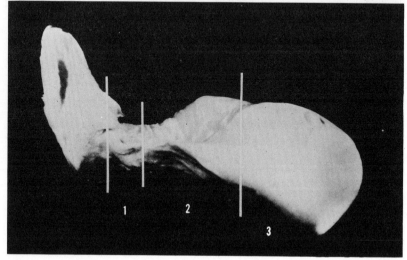

Figure 13 · A moulage of a vagina, seen from the lateral (side) view, with the pubococcygeus muscle in a contracted state. The dished appearance at the top of area 2 is the indentation of the urinary bladder. Area 1 is the introitus (entrance) of the vagina. (*Photograph from Dr. Kegel's case files*)

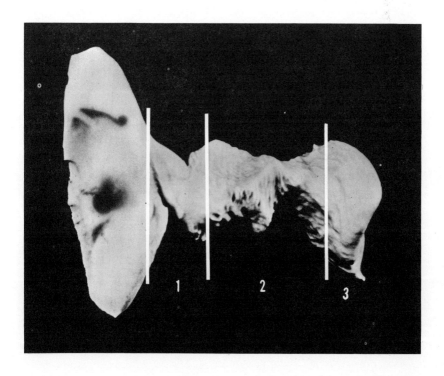

childbirth because of the stretching or injuring of the birth canal. In some Moslem countries women actually follow the appalling custom of packing the vagina with rock salt after giving birth, in order to make it contract.

After their study of sexual response in many societies, Ford and Beach concluded: "There is considerable evidence to support the belief that distention of the vaginal walls resulting from insertion of the penis is an important factor."

Widespread reports now confirm this conclusion. Dr. Donald Hastings, of the University of Minnesota, comments: "The exercise and contraction of the voluntary muscles which form the pelvic floor and surround parts of the vagina are important for . . . enhancement of sexual pleasure." He adds, "Some of the 'secret' sexual practices of other cultures depend upon the strength and cultivation of the vaginal muscles."

And Dr. John F. Oliven, of New York's Columbia Presbyterian Hospital, reports in his textbook on sexual problems for physicians and other professionals: "The most important hypesthesic [lack-of-feeling] syndrome occurs in connection with vaginal over-relaxation. To the patient herself this may appear to be a matter of insufficient contact between penis and vaginal walls. However, there is evidence that relaxed walls are hypesthesic walls, because the sub-mucosal 'deep-touch' nerve endings which are responsible for the greater part of so-called vaginal sensation are minimally represented if their vehicle—chiefly the pubococcygeus—is hypotrophic [weak through underdevelopment or degeneration]."

Oliven ends by saying, "Thus, probably no degree of 'bulk immission' can completely overcome these women's diminished sensation." In other words, when the vaginal walls do not contract so that they offer pressure and resistance, sensation is likely to be limited indeed, regardless of the size of the male organ.

Figure 14 · (*Left*) An artist's conception of vagina, seen from above, showing good muscle development. The heavy lines indicate strong muscle fibers which are here exaggerated to suggest the thickness and resistance of the pubococcygeus muscle which make possible better vaginal perception. (*Right*) An artist's conception of the vagina, seen from above, showing poor muscle development. The lines indicating muscle here are lighter and sparser, suggesting the thinness and lack of resistance of the pubococcygeus muscle usually accompanied by poor vaginal perception. Note how much wider are the poorly supported vaginal and urinary passages.

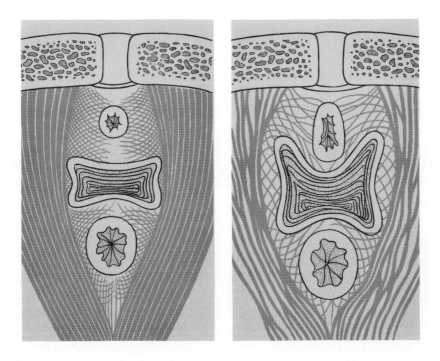

That there are wide variations in P.C. muscle strength is demonstrated by a special device. Called the perineometer, it was developed by Dr. Kegel and approved by the American Medical Association.

The perineometer is a pressure-sensitive tube attached to a meter. The tube is inserted into the vagina, and the patient is asked to exert pressure on it. Most women will contract the P.C. with pressures that give readings from 5 to perhaps 15. But women with normally strong muscle can register pressure from a minimum of 30 to as much as 90.

Those women in whom a vaginal mold shows the typical signs of poor P.C. strength develop low pressure readings on the perineometer. Those who show good readings also evidence the characteristic narrow molds which indicate good strength and support.

The exercises which strengthen the P.C. muscle are safe, simple and not fatiguing. Aside from the sexual benefit they seem to provide, they improve the support given to the organs of the pelvis. Such support has been found by experts to reduce the number of childbirth injuries to the mother and to shorten the time of delivery, thus increasing safety for the child.

Proponents of natural childbirth see such exercise as essential. And even many doctors who are not in favor of natural childbirth feel that this muscular training is valuable. Instructors who teach the Y.W.C.A. classes in preparing for childbirth give the exercises to the pregnant women they train. And the International Childbirth Education Association has made the exercises part of its programs of instruction.

But for the vast majority of the many thousands of women who have now learned the exercises, there is meaning beyond health and safety.

6

---

learning

muscular control

THOUGH a few doctors long ago suspected the importance of the pelvic floor muscles, they knew little of how to improve them. Dr. Robert Dickinson found most women were unaware of having such muscle and certainly had no voluntary control over it.

Some observers had even noted that beyond the role of the muscle in enhancing intercourse and promoting feminine orgasm, the P.C. itself, in an ultimate series of sharp contractions, was the chief physical signal of the orgasm, whether the orgasm was induced internally or externally. Indeed, in modern laboratory work, Dr. William Masters has shown that contraction of the pelvic floor muscles is the first and probably foremost physical reaction of feminine response.

In 1944, writing in the *Psychiatric Quarterly*, Edmund Bergler observed: "The involuntary contraction of the pelvic and perineal muscles at the end of the sex act is the one and only sure criterion that a man can use to determine whether a woman is frigid." Then he adds, "Over the muscles involved in these she has no conscious control."

While it is indeed true that the orgasmic contractions are involuntary, these muscles are now well known to be controllable by conscious wish. One can make an imperfect comparison to certain muscles of the leg. By tapping the knee, the doctor can make the leg jerk in an involuntary reaction. But the same muscles are moved by conscious control with the greatest of ease.

Dickinson commented early that, with instruction, "nearly all" women could be taught to contract the muscle. But the technique of strengthening the muscle remained something of a puzzle.

Some German physicians advised patients to lift the loins, then consciously contract the outer muscle of the anus. The process was fatiguing and had little effect.

Like Dickinson, Van de Velde taught patients the feeling of the muscle by touching it during examination with a finger (see Figure 15). He tried to get pregnant patients to practice contraction of the muscle twice a day. When he succeeded in the instruction, these women showed "remarkable improvement." He urged his fellow specialists in women's disorders to take advantage of every gynecological examination "to be of help to their patients in this way as well." But most doctors ignored the advice.

Many women can contract the P.C. on conscious command by merely learning it exists. And Dr. Kegel has pointed out that some women can achieve satisfaction for the first time just by being made aware of the muscle and its role in the sex act.

But if the muscle is weak, as it is in most women, awareness is unlikely to be enough. Not only must the woman learn conscious control of the muscle; she must strengthen it with exercise. "And it is a rare woman," says Dr. Kegel, "who cannot benefit from increased strength of the muscle."

Gaining control, however, can be difficult without guidance. Most women, when they are asked to contract the vaginal muscles, begin by trying to contract the smaller, weaker, *external* muscles

Figure 15 · How the doctor examines the pubococcygeus muscle. (*Left*) When the muscle has good tone, resistance is felt in all directions. (*Right*) When the muscle has poor tone, the vagina is roomy and the thin walls feel as though detached from surrounding structures.

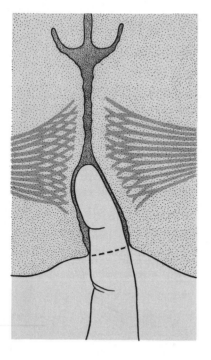
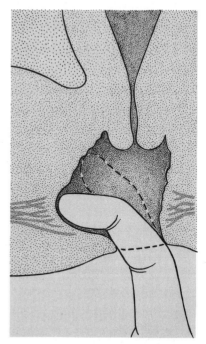

instead. This may be seen in a kind of pursing of the vaginal opening.

Asked to try again, and reminded that this is *internal* muscle, many make greater and greater efforts, contracting muscles of the abdomen, the lower back, the hips and thighs. These muscles have no link to the P.C. And, in fact, one may be certain that the exercise is done incorrectly if one experiences muscle fatigue.

(There is muscle which appears indirectly linked to the P.C. —the rectus muscle of the abdomen. This muscle, actually a pair of muscles, makes a straight band from the pubic bone to the rib cage and is a major part of the abdominal wall. It has been noted to contract mildly when the P.C. is contracted. In the shark, the rectus muscles are one with the P.C., and there is some speculation that early in man's evolution his muscular anatomy may have been similar to the shark's. In man, of course, the pubic bone now separates the two muscles, but there still appears to be some nerve association between the two. And it is interesting to observe some of the similarities of function, as each walls off a body cavity and supports the organs within, though in different ways.)

To determine whether or not a woman contracts the P.C., the doctor may ask her to contract the muscle while lying on her back, knees flexed upward and apart. If she does so, the doctor can see the perineum (the area below the vaginal opening, between it and the anus) rise.

The woman might make the same observation, using a mirror. But it can be hard for the untrained to distinguish between the upward movement of the perineum and the pursing effect of the contraction of the external muscles of the vagina.

Some childbirth educators use the perineometer, the device for measuring the strength of the P.C. A rise on the meter proves the contraction has been achieved. This method also teaches the woman what a contraction feels like so that she can recognize when it is correctly done.

There are two other methods. The doctor can ask the patient to contract while he examines with one finger. He can feel the contraction, and can show the location of the muscle by pressing against it. A woman might do this herself, but there is the hazard of infection and also of confusing an external with an internal contraction.

To teach the patient how to contract the muscle, what it feels like and how to check it at home, Dr. Kegel devised another way. This is the simplest and best for an individual.

Remember that, among other functions, the P.C. can control the voiding of urine. So if urination can be interrupted, the P.C. has been contracted.

However, since the weaker external muscles can also shut off urine flow, except under stress, these must be kept out of play. To do so, the knees are widely separated. In this position, once flow has begun, an effort is made to stop it.

In nearly all women, this effort automatically contracts the P.C. This signifies little about strength, for the muscle can stop urine flow in most women unless there is extra stress. But it teaches the feeling of a P.C. contraction. After a few trials, most women can recognize the sensation and can repeat the contractions at any time, anywhere, using the occasional interruption of voiding only as a check. Each contraction exercises the muscle surrounding the vagina.

There is little physical effort, though concentration is needed at first. "Once the contraction is learned," says childbirth educator Dr. Mary Jane Hungerford, "it takes little more effort than to close an eye. In fact, it can be done as rapidly as you open and shut an eye, though when exercising, the contraction should be held for about two seconds."

Once control of the P.C. is learned, women are instructed to begin exercise with five or ten contractions before arising in the morning. The contraction seems to be easier at this time.

And at first, the exercise should also be tried whenever urine is voided. "With good control," says Dr. Hungerford, "urine can be released a teaspoon at a time."

How much exercise is needed? The plan can be varied widely, but a usual recommendation is for some ten contractions in a row, made at six intervals during the day. This makes sixty contractions in all. Though it may sound laborious, each contraction need take no more than a second. Each group of ten contractions might take ten seconds. Six such sessions in a day would make a total of one minute.

Gradually, the number of sessions and the number of contractions made in each can be increased. For example, twenty contractions in a session would bring the six-session total to a hundred and twenty a day. Dr. Kegel suggests that each voiding of urine be an opportunity for exercise. If this is done three times a day, adding exercise before arising, when retiring and at one other time, the initial program is completed. (However, Dr. Kegel often suggests that the day's exercise be done in three twenty-minute periods.)

This program should then be stepped up, for the contraction becomes almost effortless. Many women find that thirty contractions in a session is a comfortable number, and can be done in a minute once training is under way. There is no rush to increase, but eventually most women find that two hundred and three hundred contractions a day are easily achieved, spaced throughout the day at convenient times. This would make a total of three hundred contractions in the day's exercise. Dr. Kegel says most patients reach a total of about three hundred a day in some six weeks. By this time, control of voiding is usually very good, though in some women with especially weak musculature ten weeks might be needed. Most women can note sexual and other changes within three weeks, but nevertheless are urged to continue.

How long? After six to eight weeks, when the three hundred-a-day pattern has been reached, further exercise is usually not necessary. One reason is that the normal state of the P.C. is not full relaxation. To do its job of pelvic support, it stays in a state of partial contraction and tends to maintain its strength. Without such partial contraction, for example, urine would not normally be retained. The P.C. relaxes completely only under anesthesia.

The exercises strengthen this steady state of contraction. After a few weeks, a mold of the vagina shows a markedly changed shape. Moreover, sexual activity helps preserve the new muscle tone in several ways.

First, it appears that the steady-state contraction is heightened during intercourse. Second, sexual stimulation seems to produce mild reflex contractions of the vaginal muscles. Third, many experts counsel women to make occasional conscious contractions as a technique of intercourse, as we shall see in greater detail. Finally, in sexual climax, the P.C. contracts involuntarily, strongly and rhythmically, from four to ten times, at intervals of about four-fifths of a second. (The feeling of release and the disappearance of tension follow this contractile burst.)

Women who have difficulty in determining whether or not they contract the P.C. are taught to do so at first only while voiding urine. Other women, who seem to have little sense of the position and existence of the muscle, may need a doctor's help in learning to exercise.

At the American Institute of Family Relations, women are counseled to use the new contractile ability in intercourse consciously at first, squeezing firmly and slowly. In fact, a series of conscious contractions are recommended before the entrance of the male organ. This is thought to help set the stage for the function of the muscle as an automatic reflex. And it appears to heighten sexual tension, which is desirable, since it is the build-up of such tension which, reaching a summit, seems to trigger the orgasm.

In some cases, patients are advised to fantasy while learning the exercise. This seems to condition an association between the contractions and lovemaking. Gradually, the contractions become a way to participate.

Participation by the woman is among the most important of modern concepts of successful physical love. Speaking of this, Dr. Charles Lloyd, a leading sex authority, comments that in our society "adult women are often incapable of sexual aggressions and assume an inactive role during marital intercourse. Frequently they do not experience clear-cut orgasms." Societies in which there is training for the sexual role, he points out, "usually produce a higher degree of aggressiveness in sexual activity with vigorous participation by the woman and much more regularly complete and satisfactory orgasm."

The use of the P.C. muscle provides a clear mechanism for such participation. It offers a concept of the vagina, not merely as a passive receiver of action, but as an actor.

Some forty years ago, Van de Velde described this concept: "The whole structure (of the female organs) accentuated by the working of the . . . muscles . . . is an apparatus for gripping and rubbing the male sexual organ, during and after its insertion or immission into the vagina, and thus to produce the ejaculation of seed or sperm-cells, in the culmination of excitement, and at the same time, by pressure and friction, to ensure this orgasm, or some of pleasure and ecstasy, in the woman also."

How intrinsic in intercourse is this pattern? Some reports indicate that it occurs through simply an awareness and strengthening of the vaginal musculature.

According to Dr. Hungerford:

"In childbirth education we teach the contraction exercises in order to strengthen the birth canal, and to help the canal distend more easily so that pain and injury for the mother can be avoided. At first, in teaching the exercises, I made no mention of the sexual value. I taught them only in terms of childbirth.

"But within weeks after I began teaching, one woman took me aside before class to say she had experienced orgasm in intercourse for the first time. The same thing has happened repeatedly. Many women seem to think this was the most important thing they got from the courses and report they have taught others with the same result.

"Some years ago a marriage-counselor colleague, a woman of sixty, observed my class and listened as I taught the exercises. By now I was explaining the sexual importance, and the counselor questioned me about this. When I saw her a month later, she threw her arms around me and said that for the first time in forty years of marriage, she had experienced a full orgasm."

The exercises seem able to restore sexual adjustment which has been lost, apparently through the extreme stretching of the P.C. during childbirth. As Dr. John Oliven explains: "If it [the P.C.] is constitutionally predisposed to weakness, it may not regain normal tonus, even following relatively normal childbirth, and especially after several childbirths in succession."

In addition to such stretching, there can be other problems, which are common indeed. First, when a woman has never given birth, there is a special structure of tissue just below the opening to the vagina. Called the fourchette, it is a ridge which forms the bottom margin of the external sex organs in women. In childbirth, the opening of the vagina usually cannot stretch enough to permit the baby to pass. To prevent the bordering tissues from tearing, the doctor generally makes a surgical cut, through the fourchette.

This makes the opening to the vagina more slack. The result is that the male organ now supplies less stimulation.

(Obstetricians are increasingly aware of another problem which may be caused by the necessary cutting of the fourchette, which is known as an episiotomy. If the cut is made improperly, it may damage the P.C. As Dr. Oliven indicates in his summary: "Medio-lateral episiotomy today—partly because of its use increasingly early during the second stage of labor—tends to cause major damage to the pubococcygeal muscle on one side. . . . Such an unrepaired muscle appears to be a major contributor to unsatisfactory sexual function.")

Rather profound damage to the muscle can also be done by the baby's normal passage through the vaginal canal. If the musculature surrounding the vagina is poor, the canal becomes flaccid and weak. As the baby pushes through, the vaginal walls may be pinched and even torn, and the surrounding muscle is simultaneously badly stretched to still greater weakness. Often the problem grows worse with each succeeding delivery. This is one reason why urinary stress incontinence may appear after several children have been born to a woman who had no such difficulties before.

Some doctors recommend that their patients exercise during pregnancy to give the walls greater strength and tonus. Like other muscles, the P.C. actually thickens with exercise. For similar reasons, doctors also use the exercises restoratively, after delivery.

If, as Dr. Kegel suggests, perhaps two-thirds of American women have P.C. muscle weakness enough to interfere with sexual function, one would expect that childbirth injuries associated with weak muscle, along with other medical groups of P.C. weakness, would be common indeed. There are indications that this is the fact.

In his *Handbook of Obstetrics and Gynecology*, Dr. Ralph Benson, chairman of the Department of Obstetrics and Gynecology at the University of Oregon Medical School, writes: "Slight degrees of urinary stress incontinence are noted in 50–60 percent of females in all age groups; most cases occur in women who have suffered childbirth injuries or who have developed weakness of the pelvic floor structures during menopause. About 20 percent of major elective gynecologic surgical procedures are partially or wholly for the purpose of correcting this annoying disorder."

Another common related problem is illustrated by the case of Ellen F. At thirty-four, a year after the birth of her fourth child, she complained of pain in intercourse. The sex act had never been very satisfactory for her, but now it was distinctly unpleasant.

On examination, the doctor found a condition called rectocele. The wall of the vagina, repeatedly damaged and weakened in childbirth, had gradually given way to pressure from the rectum, which lies very close behind it and can exert much pressure. The result was several protrusions into the vagina.

Such injury is very common. Sometimes it is not pressure from the rectum which causes the protrusion, but pressure from the urinary passage (urethrocele), intestines (enterocele) or the urinary bladder (cystocele).

Dr. Benson estimates that such injuries, known as vaginal herniations, occur in at least half of all women who bear children. About one woman in ten complains of distressing symptoms. These may include bladder irritation with incomplete voiding, constipation, pain at intercourse, or a dozen other difficulties.

The injuries are not usually apparent until some time has passed after childbirth, so that obstetricians may not be aware they have occurred. Many women simply accept the discomfort as part of maternity and make little complaint. Says Dr. Benson: "Vaginal herniations are rarely observed even soon after a traumatic [injurious] delivery. The defects become apparent only months or years later, perhaps following subsequent normal deliveries."

In Ellen F.'s case, the rectocele was not severe. Surgery, which is often the only solution, was not needed. The rectocele was pressed back by the doctor. She was then given the Kegel exercises. These restored muscular tone to the vaginal walls, and this prevented more sagging, even after she had still another child. Intercourse became not only painless but satisfying.

Lois R. also complained of pain in intercourse after childbirth, but for a different reason. The P.C. muscle had torn and scarred on one side, making touch at that point painful. Though some of the scarred area of muscle could never regain much strength, exercise caused other muscle fibers to enlarge and provide some support. By an ability to sustain firm pressure, the strong side prevented the male organ from thrusting toward the sensitive area. Normal sex relations were restored.

The prevention and restoration afforded by exercise of the P.C. muscle are said by many experts to make the exercises valuable to most women at some time in life, especially for women who bear children. Good tone of the muscle is accepted widely as medically desirable. And exercise to achieve that tone is certainly harmless.

Sexually, the strengthening of the muscle and an understanding of how it functions have relieved many cases of inadequacy. And the understanding has further implications. Together with other new scientific knowledge, the concept has considerable effect on what has been believed and is now known of the art of physical love.

7

---

the gentle art

FROM early manuscripts, such as India's *Kamasutra* of the third century A.D., one can see that the art and science of love have long been rather sophisticated matters. Such ancient works were already much concerned with the problem of providing satisfaction for the woman, and suggest myriad complex avenues of touch and sound and scent. Even among primitive cultures, sexual refinements are of great concern.

So it is that anthropologists have sought in vain for "the natural way" of human lovemaking. It appears that virtually no human being arrives at an age of sexual ability without a heavy burden of taboos and preconceptions about the sexual act. If there was ever an instinctive mating behavior for humans—as surely at some stage of evolution there must have been—it has been buried under layer upon layer of culture.

Mating among the lower animals appears to be highly patterned, built into the species, usually by physical and environmental factors. For example, the antelope, always in peril because he is the prey of so many beasts, couples in seconds and runs. But the bear, with no natural predators threatening, may spend a day in mating. Among humans, Dr. Ford and Dr. Beach have found, the entire sexual experience lasts only seconds in some societies, while in others there is an elaborate ritual which continues for hours.

Some cultures take infinite pains to secure satisfaction for women. The Chiricahua tribe deals with the problem by disallowing it, holding that women should display no emotions in the sex act. The Colorado Indians and such primitive cultures as that of the Lepcha insist that the woman remain entirely passive, thus making her pleasure unlikely.

Ford and Beach comment: "Men and women do not develop their individual patterns of sexual behavior simply as a result of biological heredity. Human sexual responses are not instinctive in the sense of being determined exclusively by the actions of genes and chromosomes. On the contrary, from the first years of life, every child is taught about sex, either directly or indirectly. And most significant is the fact that different societies teach different lessons in this regard."

In one respect, however, most societies agree. Only a few of even the most primitive cultures make of the woman a mere instrument. Love is the universal element, and to give pleasure to one's love and to value the reassuring response to physical affection are almost universal desires. To this end, many systems have been invented.

Ancient lore is rife with sexual philters and spells and potions. Some of these are still sold in certain American cities of the South, and in modern spray cans. But science finds that there is no such thing known as an aphrodisiac, a drug which arouses passion. The sole exception seems to be the male hormones which are given to women for certain disorders, many of whom experience increased desire. Such hormones are not prescribed for sexual purposes, since the sexual effect is not dependable and the drugs produce many profound bodily changes.

Many people believe that narcotics induce keener sexuality.

But, on the contrary, they tend to deplete both potency and desire. Alcohol, like narcotics, is likely to dim sensation and decrease adequacy, though of course it may remove psychological inhibitions.

An old belief, but still surprisingly current, is the idea that certain foods have sexual effects. In a large area of France, the truffle is believed by many educated people to enhance desire and potency, a belief which dates from Roman times. Several hundred years ago, lettuce was considered to be stimulating. When the tomato was first introduced into Europe, it was called the "love apple." Today, on many Caribbean islands, local folk ascribe sexual powers to the meat of the conch, whose large swirling shell produces a sound like ocean surf. And even in much of the United States, many still believe in the sexual effect of certain other seafoods, especially oysters. Sadly, none of these ideas has proven correct.

Poets and novelists have created much belief in secrets of technique, possessed by harem girls of the East, rakes and courtesans. But all of those which science encounters prove disappointing. For example, let us look at some of the "secrets" of the famed *Koka Shastra* of the twelfth century which are still practiced in India today. One section begins: "On the armpits, the arms, the thighs, the pubic region, the breasts and neck, a couple of fiery disposition will make nailmarks . . . The nails of passionate lovers should have large, strong tips . . ." Several types of scratches and marks are recommended. There are half moons and "definite scratches two or three thumb-breadths long." There is "the hare jump, made by catching the breast around the nipple with all five nails together." And there are times to scratch: "Three or four deep scratches on the pubic region or the breasts are prescribed by experts before parting on foreign travel, as a keepsake."

Bites are also detailed and named, as "a long deep double-row of toothprints with a dark-red bruise between them, proper to the convexity of the breasts, [which] is the boar-mark." There are prescriptions, too, for blows. Generally, the aim is for variety of physical stimulation, from which mild pain is certainly not barred.

The problem of feminine orgasm is dealt with, in one effort, by adjusting caresses to the phases of the moon. For example, it is written that on the thirteenth lunar day, "she will come quickly to orgasm by kissing her cheeks, pulling upon her left breast, and slowly scratching her neck with the fingernails."

Such ideas are not merely amusing antiquities. Many manuals of sexual practice still advocate maneuvers which are equally surprising. Consider *The Marriage Art*, by Dr. John E. Eichenlaub, which by December of 1967 was in its nineteenth printing, totaling over 1,500,000 copies.

Eichenlaub, a medical doctor, in one section describes some "celebration specials" which he suggests "if your partner shows signs of tapering enthusiasm or slow arousal, or if you just want to give him a special thrill on some festive occasion . . ." One of these is the "ice-spurred special." Before intercourse, one partner places by the bedside a bowl of crushed ice. The ice-holder waits until orgasm has begun for the partner, whereupon he "jams the ice-cold poultice" between the legs of the partner.

Modern research finds that such complex, mechanical approaches to sex can actually do serious psychological damage. Most experts have discarded the "sex secrets," which are so much heralded, in favor of a rather uncontrived intimacy in which both partners simply are aware of the physiologic facts of human mating. Let us examine what science has learned of sexual technique.

We have noted that there is no universal pattern of arousing women to intercourse. Certainly, however, some preparation is needed. For men are ready for intercourse very quickly, while women are slower to develop the physical changes which pave the way for satisfaction.

(This time difference in response to sexual stimulation does not seem entirely intrinsic to the male or female body. Kinsey reports on the self-stimulation of 2,114 women. He finds that in this manner, women reach orgasm in a time rather similar to that of men. These time differences are examined more closely in a later chapter.)

Sexual preparation seems to be different for each woman, and for the same woman on different occasions. One explanation is that, in human beings, the most recently developed areas of the brain appear to control sexual behavior. These are the areas most dependent upon learning and the intellect.

Because human experience and conditioning are so varied, there is no single system of preparation that is infallible. And marriage counselors find that one of the most common sources of sexual maladjustment is the failure of women to tell their husbands frankly, clearly and precisely what stimulates them. Instead, most couples appear to rely upon a pattern, and often one which they think is conventional. And a kiss or touch which is usually stimulating can become meaningless and even unwanted. Ritual is inimical to the spontaneity of love. It does not suit the ever-changing reactiveness of the human mind and body. Perhaps some such changes can be intuited by the partner, but verbal communication is a good deal more reliable. And the very expression of erotic wishes can enhance the experience by heightening the sense of intimacy.

Moreover, physical manipulation is not the only preparatory route. Affecting words, music or situations may already have set the stage, and prolonged preparation, simply because it is the usual pattern, may actually be destructive. Experts have observed that for the woman who understands her role in intercourse, and has learned to respond to it, there are often times when very little preparation is needed.

Surveys show that in terms of preparatory stimulation only one kind approaches being universal; this is the stimulation by the man of the external sex organs of the woman. Yet more than a few women are known who, capable of full response, nevertheless frankly dislike this maneuver.

Ideally, though preparation of the woman is usually seen as a means to an end, it is best regarded as a period of preliminary affection of equal pleasure and interest to the man and not merely as a duty to be performed. Further, the vast majority of women are stimulated, not merely by receiving preliminary affection, but by giving it. They should take full part. One of the interesting observations made by recent sex researchers denies what was once considered to be a basic precept of preliminary lovemaking. Because men were seen to reach orgasm so much more quickly than women, it was felt that the woman should refrain from very direct stimulation of her husband before intercourse. Actually, it has been observed that the contrary is usually true, that the man is more likely to reach satisfaction prematurely when he goes unstimulated through a long period of preparatory arousal of the woman.

One explanation for this phenomenon is in the nature of orgasm itself, which is seen as the explosive culmination of rising tension. When the man is the sole actor, his chief interest becomes anticipation of the time when the woman will be ready for intercourse. This anticipation builds his tension to a point at which he is very likely to respond prematurely almost as soon as intercourse begins. On the other hand, effective sexual stimulation given him (within the limits we will examine when we consider the sexual difficulties of men) actually helps to hold him at a plateau. Seen psychologically, he is receiving pleasurable sensations, which sustain his selfish interest in preparatory lovemaking. His attention is taken away from an anxious awaiting of intercourse. Even direct stimulation of the male organ is desirable as a part of preparation, when seen in this light. And we shall explain how, if such direct stimulation does proceed too far, the sexual tension of the male organ can be quickly reduced.

This finding is important because it removes a key block to the woman's full participation and helps to keep physical intimacy a mutual experience. It also allows the woman to play an active role through all phases of the intimacy, so that she is more likely to continue her participation during intercourse when it is essential. If she must stop her participation as physical love reaches a more exciting stage, it becomes difficult for her to change her role, from passive to active, as intercourse begins. Finally, in giving pleasure, the woman further heightens her own sexual tension desirably, and she is able to maintain the constant attention which seems to be important to her. As Kinsey noted, along with many others, the female of all species seems to be easily distracted from sex. He writes: "When the steady build-up of the female's response is interrupted by the male's cessation of movement, changes of position, conversation, or temporary withdrawal from the genital union, she drops back to or toward a normal physiologic state from which she has to start again." When the woman is active in the preparatory stage, her attention is less likely to be diverted.

What are the limits of preliminary affection? Doctors, psychiatrists and marriage counselors agree there are virtually none, that there are no "perversions" within wide boundaries. These boundaries seem to be simply that whatever is enjoyed be pleasurable to both, that the pleasure of one not depend on the pain of the other, and that the experience customarily end with intromission, the entrance of the male organ into the vagina.

In one sense, many researchers have observed that the sex act follows a vague pattern for most women, one which is seen to be a kind of repetition of the sexual development of the individual. The youngest infant responds to physical closeness and warmth. Then the adolescent girl responds to kisses and caresses. She also is conditioned to associate this physical affection with romantic situations and ideas, with the result that such associations lead her toward more sexual activity.

Early in development, almost any adolescent girl responds to stimulation of the clitoris and other organs of the vulva with a kind of climax which is physically indistinguishable from more mature climax. The vast majority of American girls experiment, in fact, with self-stimulation of the external genitals, though rarely with the stimulation of the vagina. Finally, as a woman, the response to vaginal stimulation in intercourse is learned.

This development is repeated in the typical sex act, moving from romantic association and physical affection to external genital stimulation, and ending in intercourse. Physically, authorities say there is scarcely a woman who is not capable of such experience. And, in general, it is concluded that any woman who responds to physical affection with lubrication of the vagina and engorgement of the sex organs should also be able to attain a full climax. Let us see how this climax is understood to come about.

We have seen the engorgement, accompanied by mounting muscular tension, which takes place throughout the body during sexual stimulation. This engorgement is known as tumescence, and it takes place over a much wider bodily area than many people realize. After a study of the literature, Kinsey summed up: "The surface outlines of the whole body of one who is sexually aroused become quite different from the outlines of one who is not so aroused. The lobes of the ears may become thickened and swollen. The lips of the mouth may become filled with blood and, in most individuals, more protrudent than in ordinary circumstances . . . The anal area may become turgid. The arms and the legs may have their outlines altered. The tumescence is so apparent everywhere over the body that it alone is sufficient evidence of the presence of erotic arousal."

Scarcely a muscle of any importance escapes the general pattern of tension. Even the eye muscles are involved, along with those of the neck, chest, back, arms and legs, hands and feet, abdomen, buttocks, thighs and pelvis. "One of the most striking aspects of a sexual performance," says Kinsey, "is the development of neuromuscular [nerve-muscle] tensions throughout the body . . . From head to toe, the muscles contract and relax, in steady or more convulsive rhythms . . . Sometimes the movements are violent. Sometimes they are so limited that they are hardly noticeable."

Adding to these tensions are those of circulation and breathing. The pulse commonly doubles. Breathing becomes deeper and more rapid. Blood pressure in intercourse has been measured at levels equal to severe hypertension. Measurements of brain waves show bold rhythmic peaks which evidence the building of a kind of electrical storm in the body. Each of these factors rebounds against the others to intensify the total effect. The phenomenon has been likened to what happens in the earth's atmosphere when stores of electrical energy accumulate until they have reached a peak and are released in a lightning bolt.

In sexual experience, Dr. William Masters describes the growing tension state as an "orgasmic platform." This platform can be produced to some extent even by thoughts. In all but a few women it can be reached through physical stimulation. But once the male organ enters, the build-up stops for many women. For others, the platform may be sustained, perhaps with some increase of tension; but for some reason that tension never reaches the peak that triggers the four to ten muscular contractions which are the core of sexual climax.

Experts conclude that for virtually all women the initial phases of the orgasmic platform are an almost automatic response to effective emotional and physical stimulation. If the external stimulation, especially of the clitoris and other parts of the vulva, continues, orgasm is the almost universal result. But to continue the build-up of sexual tension after intercourse begins, authorities agree, is an ability which must be *learned*.

Moreover, this heightened tension during intercourse must be actively *sought* by the woman, not passively awaited. For most women, no amount of skill or technique on the part of the husband will suffice. The woman must not merely surrender to her husband, she must surrender to her own drive, a drive to seek stimulation emotionally and physically, to seek tension until tension becomes release.

Some women are enabled to attain orgasm simply by adopting this attitude. Many authorities believe this is in large part because the woman, in giving herself over to the pursuit of release, becomes more responsive to her own subtle physical sensations and learns to move her body so as to increase the sensations. For most women, however, a fuller understanding of how stimulation occurs in intercourse appears to be the key.

Here we reach the question of how the vagina plays its role in intercourse, so that stimulation culminates in climax. We have seen how this problem has puzzled science. In 1948, Kinsey expressed the general opinion when he wrote: "The literature usually implies that the vagina itself should be the center of sensory stimulation, and this as we have seen is a physical and physiologic impossibility for nearly all females."

Kinsey is speaking of studies concerned with the problem of determining which parts of the body are responsive to sexual stimulation by observing where the subjects could perceive a light, gentle touch. Only 14 percent of women in the study Kinsey mentions felt such a touch on the walls of the vagina.

We know that the deep-touch nerves in the P.C. muscle respond only to firm touch, that they do not perceive well unless they offer resistance to the stimulus, and that a majority of women do not have the muscle tone which provides very good resistance. These facts probably help to account for the results which were found.

Despite this conclusion of Kinsey's, however, we find this note elsewhere in his writing: "A ring of powerful muscles lies just beyond the vaginal entrance . . . [He describes these as the "levators," another name for the P.C.] The female may be very conscious of pressure on the levators. The muscles may respond reflexly when they are stimulated by pressure, and most females are erotically aroused when they are so stimulated."

Kinsey also writes, summarizing his search of the literature: "On the other hand, many females, and perhaps a majority of them, find that when coitus [intercourse] involves deep vaginal penetrations, they secure a type of satisfaction which differs from that provided by the stimulation of the labia or clitoris alone. In view of the evidence that the walls of the vagina are ordinarily insensitive, it is obvious that the satisfactions obtained from vaginal penetration must depend on some mechanism that lies outside of the vaginal walls themselves."

We now know more of what that mechanism is. And, while not all the mysteries have been solved, we also know much more about how to promote the mechanism.

First, let us look at the kind of nerves which are stimulated in intercourse. True vaginal stimulation affects a kind of cluster of nerve cells called proprioceptors, which respond chiefly to such stimuli as pressing and stretching.

Try this experiment. Straighten one of your fingers, tensing it.

Then slowly curl it up as tightly as you can. Straighten and curl it a few times more, slowly, deliberately and with effort. You will feel very clearly the impressions of changing position, along with the stretch and contraction of the muscles. The nerve endings which provide those sensations are similar to the ones in the musculature surrounding the vagina.

Now make the same finger motions as rapidly as you can, and you will see that the sensations become vaguer and more blurred. This suggests the one falseness of notion about feminine stimulation in intercourse—the idea that vigorous friction produces vigorous stimulation. The truth is that slow movement is felt more clearly. Vigorous friction as soon as the male organ enters is almost a guarantee that sensation will be blurred and that sexual tension will actually decline.

When motion in intercourse is rapid friction, the thrusting force is in line with the male organ. Thus, it is dissipated toward the depths of the vagina, the least sensitive area. The vaginal walls are not much pressed against. And if vigorous penetration goes deep, it may cause distracting discomfort through collision with the cervix, the mouth of the womb. While rapid, vigorous friction is likely to suppress the woman's sensation, slowing her reactions or even stopping them, it *heightens* male sensations in an unwanted way by precipitating the man toward rapid climax. For the nerves in the skin of the penis are like those of the clitoris, responding all too well to light, frictional stimulation.

Counselors at the American Institute of Family Relations have formulated a plan for learning good technique which seems most helpful to both partners. Once the woman has learned the contraction exercises, the couple is advised to begin intercourse with a slow, gentle entrance, following which there is no motion at all.

Instead, at first the woman uses conscious contraction of the P.C. muscle. This teaches her more about the kind of sensation she can receive from the vagina. It helps her to focus her attention on vaginal sensation, a most important factor. And at the same time, it provides a rich form of stimulation for her partner, but one which does not tend to speed him toward his orgasm. It is possible to have satisfying intercourse in this manner alone, though thrusting seems almost a reflex reaction for both as climax nears.

It is important for women to know that as they learn vaginal techniques for their own satisfaction they in no way cheat the male. As it is explained in the Indian *Ananga Ranga* of the sixteenth century: "She must ever strive to close and constrict the Yoni [vagina] until she holds the Lingam [penis] as with a finger, opening and shutting at her pleasure, and finally acting as the hand of the Gopala-girl, who milks the cow. This can be learned only by long practice, and especially by throwing the will into the part affected. . . . Her husband will then value her above all women, nor would he exchange her for the most beautiful queen in the Three Worlds. So lovely and pleasant to the man is she-who-constricts."

Interestingly, Richard Burton, in his nineteenth-century translation, notes: "Such an artist is called by the Arabs *Kabbazah*, literally a 'holder,' and it is not surprising that the slave dealers pay large sums for her. All women have more or less the power, but they wholly neglect it."

Following such a quiet period of contraction, it is suggested that both partners develop something of a mutual, gentle motion, aimed at applying pressure to the vaginal walls. This gives some stimulation to the nerves outside the walls. It also teaches the woman to begin seeking her gratification by adjusting her own movements, and it accustoms her partner to leaving her physically free to move. By experimenting with these gentle motions, the woman begins to learn what kind of activity on her part sustains or increases the sexual tension she wishes to build to climax.

During this motion, the woman is encouraged to use some voluntary contractions, to increase the resistance of the vaginal walls and promote stimulation. These contractions soon become an automatic reflex, which heightens the effectiveness of any technique by increasing the contact of the penis with the walls. The conscious effort at first helps to set this pattern. Some of the involuntary contraction which results from stimulation further tightens the P.C.'s constant partially contracted state, keeping the vagina narrowed during intercourse. Some of the reflex tends to be more sharply spasmodic, almost like a kind of preliminary orgasm. Remember, ultimately these same muscles contract sharply and profoundly in the involuntary spasms which *are* orgasm. Using them heightens their tension and potentiates the final release.

This does not mean that the more conventional piston-like thrusting of intercourse is without value. But such training makes clear the importance of slow and deliberate movement. And it encourages a more rotary motion of the hips of the partners, along with the thrusting. This sort of rotation, in a circular, forward-and-back motion, again helps to turn some of the pressure of the thrust away from the end of the vagina and toward the more responsive vaginal walls.

There is no intent here to specify the kinds of motion which are appropriate. For what is important is the basic concept of interposing resistance to the movement of the male organ, in moving slowly and gently so that response can be felt, and in this way seeking maximum stimulation.

Nature assists this resistance. The walls of the vagina are not smooth but ridged. Excitement engorges these walls and accentuates the ridging, as contraction draws the walls together. The male organ, in pushing the walls apart and pressing the ridges aside, gives full stimulation. The slow, deliberate movement may become more vigorous toward climax, but the orgasmic platform has now reached a tense pitch in which sensation is greater. At the same time, the involuntary contractions of the muscles become stronger, offering greater resistance and greater stimulation.

In his measurements, made during feminine sexual stimulation, Masters found that the vaginal walls became "grossly distended with venous blood." As excitement proceeds, the vaginal walls, which normally lie against one another, separate, and the passage opens. But when the orgasmic platform is arrived at and the woman is ready for intercourse, the engorgement of the walls has now narrowed the opened space by a full third. The extent of this narrowing is clear in the illustration (see Figure 16), which is based upon Masters' drawings.

This engorgement and narrowing does not occur throughout the vagina. The inner portion of the passage, in fact, distends and lengthens. Masters usually describes that portion of the passage which becomes engorged as the "outer third," while Kegel often refers to that part of the vagina most affected by contractions of the P.C. muscle—and therefore the key area for contacting the penis—as the "middle third" (see Figure 17). Many scientists have thought this indicated a basic conflict between the two researchers.

Actually, Masters is writing as one who researches sex in the act. So in describing his "outer third" he includes the expanded inner portion of the vagina. Kegel, writing from the gynecologist's viewpoint, speaks of the unexpanded vagina, ending with the mouth of the womb, and thus an inch or more shorter.

Moreover, neither man seems to intend a precise "third." Measuring Masters' drawings, the orgasmic platform takes up the outer 40 percent or more of the vagina when expanded. The area would take in at least half of the vagina at rest.

If one compares the drawings of the two, one quickly sees that the engorged orgasmic platform Masters describes would include the whole of the vaginal area which is surrounded by P.C. muscle. The platform extends to the entrance of the vagina, and the P.C. does not. But in simple terms, the two phenomena seem to work together. The engorged platform becomes something like a tense pad which lines the vagina where the P.C. squeezes against the passage. The muscle presses this congested pad against the male organ, thus helping to convey movement in the vagina to the woman's external sex organs. At the same time, the orgasmic platform helps the P.C. to oppose resistance to the moving penis, thus heightening stimulation of the nerves within the muscle.

Finally, when Masters speaks of the contractions of the orgasmic platform as the signal of feminine climax, he is speaking in large part of the contracting P.C. muscle, which circles and supports the platform. Approached from either path of research, it seems clear that this area of the vagina is what doctors call the "target area." It is here that the contractions of orgasm take place and here that the most direct stimulation of intercourse seems to be received.

In practical terms, this indicates that the movement of the male organ should tend to be long as well as slow because the glans, the end of the penis, is its widest part. So it should move so as to give stimulation to the most engorged and resistive portion, roughly the first three inches, of the vagina. Counselors advise that the glans be withdrawn toward the vaginal entrance before being pressed forward. Stimulation, contrary to the belief of many men, may be just as keen during this withdrawal as during the push forward. However, the passage of the glans need not be the only stimulation. For when the vagina is in its narrowed state, the shaft of the male organ also provides movement to the engorged portion of the canal.

Figure 16· Orgasmic platform (after Masters).

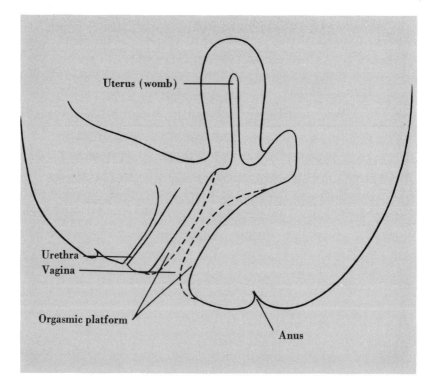

Figure 17 · Pubococcygeus muscle (after Kegel). Note how the pubococcygeus muscle encompasses the area of much of the platform, indicated by dotted line.

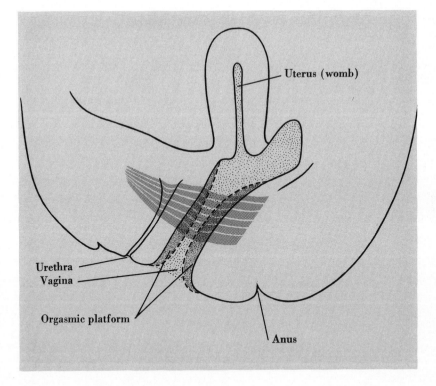

The primary need, most experts agree, is not for technical analysis of the complicated mechanics. Rather, it is for a basic understanding of how the two organs come into contact. With this understanding, if the woman seeks activity to heighten her own stimulation, she will automatically seek out the greatest sensitivity. If her partner is gentle and tries to remain sensitive and responsive to her movements, little more elaborate communication should be needed.

This concentration upon the finer sensations of the intimacy is desirable from several points of view. As Dr. Paul Popenoe advises: "Pay particular attention to sexual sensations in the vagina, eliminating all other thoughts and putting anticipation foremost in your mind. Identifying the parts of the vagina in which your sensations are most intense, you can bring these into action by moving your whole body freely."

How much difference do the relative positions of the partners make in adjusting motion and counter-motion for greatest stimulation? For centuries, position has been thought by many to be the central problem in the woman's orgasmic achievement. For this reason, most books about sexual relationships have devoted much space to refinements of position, and they often represent the varieties of position to be innumerable. Some of the Oriental texts have indeed been imaginative in the search for adjustment and sensation. Here are some examples from the *Koka Shastra:*

"If she passes her arms under her knees and round her neck, and her lover then holds her tightly about the neck, passing his arms between hers, it is known to experts as the cobra-noose.

". . . If the man sits between the forearms of a beautiful woman and takes her by repeatedly shaking his thighs, it is the friction position.

". . . If she sits in his hands with her arms round his neck and her legs round his waist, moving herself by putting the toes of one foot against the wall, throwing herself about, crying out and gasping continually, this is the suspended position."

Such positions, which in other texts are extended to refinements including the woman who stands on her head, are hardly suited to overcoming problems of satisfaction. On the contrary, they introduce a mechanistic aspect which is only likely to distract the woman from what is obviously the core of the experience.

Some rather authoritative modern texts propose positions which are only a little less ludicrous. There is certainly no harm in experiment. But if the experiment is aimed at providing satisfaction where there has been none, exaggerated postures—in fact, any position which leads to discomfort of any kind—are likely to fail. Even the commonly recommended use of a pillow under the woman's hips or loins can be distracting, and it is not likely to improve the chance of success.

Probably the main reason for the use of the pillow is the same that inspires many of the positional variations—the hope that the clitoris will be given greater stimulation by the penis. We have seen that this direct friction is difficult to achieve.

On the other hand, we do know that traction applied to some of the external organs—especially the minor lips—can be transmitted to the clitoris to heighten feeling during intercourse. We know as well that movement of the mons, the fatty tissue overlying the bony prominence of the pelvis, also is transmitted to the clitoris. The clitoris is, in fact, moored to this prominence.

These are two of the main physical reasons—though there are obvious psychological benefits as well—why face-to-face positions are usually chosen for intercourse in nearly all cultures. The Indian suggestions above are just variations of this most common technique. Among other things, in such positions, the pubic bone of the man is pressed against the mons of the woman, and the rhythmic movement is felt by the clitoris. The woman can heighten this effect by pressing toward her partner. But neither this nor any other effort should divert the woman's attention in her search for vaginal sensation. Other factors should be regarded as supplemental.

Kinsey, Pomeroy and Martin found that in our society, some 70 percent of couples use only the simplest of face-to-face positions. The woman lies on her back, knees raised and apart to make entrance easy and comfortable for both partners. The man is above her, but with his weight supported on his knees and elbows or forearms. As we have seen, it is important that the woman be free to move. The woman should also guide the small refinements of this position, the man attentive to her adjustments. Sexual movements should be very small at first, until the position is such that larger movements are certain not to cause discomfort. The couple is, after all, seeking a mutual rhythm of movement, much like partners in a dance. And many experts have pointed out that a slow evenness of rhythm seems to augment the steady growth of sexual tension in a woman. The total body seems to become involved in such a rhythm, a rising cycle of nerve-muscle tensing and release, with the end object of explosive waves of contraction. Rhythm potentiates such total-body involvement. This does not mean there are no pauses or changes in the rhythm. But it does mean that sudden or eccentric movements are likely to break the growing tension, whereas a pause need not.

A common error, however, appears to be the concentration on nothing but the climax. This merely builds anxiety. In the woman this can too easily become a fearful "Will I fail again?" In the man the question is often "Can I hold back long enough?" If either worries a great deal about the end result, the chances are good that both will fail. Anxiety is the most profound enemy of sexual release for women, and of control for men. Certainly neither partner should put pressure on the other. But above all, the partners should not pressure themselves. Summing up the view of most authorities, the art of love is in large part a selfish art of savoring each phase of the experience, seeking the maximum perception of sensation, rather than a neurotic hurrying toward release, while anxiously doubting the outcome.

There is, perhaps, a good parallel in the behavior of the true gourmet. His attention is devoted to bringing all his senses to bear upon the fullest appreciation of what is before him. He does not wolf his meal while thinking only of his after-dinner cigar. The senses belong to the very immediate and poignant present. The psychological blocks to physical love operate precisely by intruding upon the present the anger and hurt of the past and the fear of the future.

Complete attention to the sensation of the present can obviate most of the mechanism of position, especially when the woman does not wait passively to be pleased but takes an active role. And one basic variation of the most common position is often encouraged by marriage counselors to help women learn to become active.

This is the position in which the woman is above the man, straddling his hips. Kinsey found it to be the second most commonly chosen position in our culture. In this manner the woman automatically controls the direction and pace of the movement. Also, some women seem to derive great pleasure from the deepest possible penetration of the male organ. In this position such penetration is easiest to obtain, while allowing the woman control, to keep the thrust from becoming too deep or vigorous and causing discomfort.

It surprises some people to realize how few are the true departures from the basic face-to-face position. Anatomically, there is not much gross change of the relationship of male and female organs whether the couple lie down (fairly often, Kinsey found, on their sides), sit or stand. (Some recommendations are commonly seen for heightening feminine sensation by having the woman close her legs to greater or lesser degree. But in the light of newer research, this looks much like an effort to close a vaginal passage which has poor muscular tonus. It also tends to keep male penetration to a minimum and thus, perhaps, to provide more external stimulation of the woman.)

The principal exception is the entrance by the male from behind. Except for certain of the Greeks and Romans, who believed this was the "natural" position, as observed in animals, this attitude is not much used in most cultures. It is felt to deny much of the psychological pleasure and meaning of physical love, especially for the woman. However, Masters has noted that women who can reach orgasm in other positions can reach orgasm in this manner as well. This seems further evidence that position is not the crux of the matter. From what we have seen of sex research, the reasons should be clear.

In advising women who have had difficulty in reaching orgasm, most counselors suggest merely that position ought to be the most comfortable possible and leave the greatest freedom of feminine movement. The physical crux of the act is, after all, the appropriate interplay between the two primary organs.

The emotional crux in normal people seems mainly one of attitude, born of fully mutual and informed participation. Though the man is usually the aggressor in courting the woman, once intercourse has begun it requires the active behavior of both. The preliminary affection must now have moved the woman to seek the relationship just as the man does. There is no place for reticence. Once the woman has entered into the act of love, she has a role to play. If she does not play it, she cheats herself.

Some psychiatrists believe that the greatest value of Dr. Kegel's work may be the providing of a way for a woman to take a special physical part, together with what Kegel describes as "awareness of function." Once she has this awareness, she is unlikely merely to remain the passive receiver of affection, and thereby the waiting critic of her husband's skill. In the role of critic, she is likely to fail and to blame her husband's knowledge, consideration or physical ability.

Such blame quickly becomes resentment and anger. It is magnified by the man's painfully evident orgasm, leaving the woman a frustrated outsider at the climactic moment. And in a later chapter, when we discuss the meaning of research in masculine sexual difficulties, we shall see how destructive is this situation for the male, as well as for his wife.

In this all-too-common circumstance, the cycle of failure leading to blame, and blame to failure, we come upon the psychological barriers to sexual adjustment. For emotion can frustrate all of sexual knowledge and technique. It can do so even with the couple who are deeply in love, with the mature and with those who come to marriage free of neuroses. Fortunately, emotion often presents barriers which can be reduced through simple insight.

8

a perplexity
of women

ᴿECENTLY, Dr. William Masters told a meeting of the American Fertility Society that he and his colleagues could now deal with most marital sex problems in a matter of weeks. At about the same time the American Institute of Family Relations revealed similar achievements. Both credited their rather revolutionary successes to the new physical understanding above all other factors. And even those who still adhered to the view that sexual difficulty is always a symptom of underlying emotional problems were impressed. "The results," one news magazine quoted Dr. Alex Kaplan of the Psychoanalytic Foundation of St. Louis, "are pretty damn good and quick."

But even clinicians using the rapid, basically physical approach to treatment, report they must deal with psychological barriers as well. And perhaps chief among these are two common attitudes, of which it might be said that scarcely an American woman is entirely free.

These attitudes are nicely illustrated by the case of Frances Palmer, who was brought to the American Institute of Family Relations by in-law difficulties, but who was also sexually unresponsive. The doctor to whom the Institute sent Mrs. Palmer found a weakness of the pelvic muscles and great lack of information. He moved to correct both, but Frances still failed to reach orgasm.

Talking to her counselor about the persisting sex difficulty, Mrs. Palmer said: "I just can't get enthusiastic about this exercise and the like. I want things to improve, but this doesn't seem the right way. I keep feeling the answer is for Alan to learn more, to think more of my feelings and less of his own pleasure. It just doesn't seem feminine to work at this the way you ask me to."

The counselor interviewed Alan Palmer and learned that he was deeply troubled by the failure and had tried hard to help Frances overcome it. "I just don't know what more I can do," he said.

Then the counselor probed Frances' upbringing. Like most American girls, she had been trained to reticence. And in her small Southern town, feminine modesty and reserve had been stressed still more.

"I think my earliest memory must be of Mother saying, 'Now, Frances, remember you're a lady.' I was never allowed to play boys' games or be alone with them. I had to have a clean face and wear a skirt, and I envied boys the freedom they had, to do what they wanted to do."

To some extent American girls learn early that the male has his privileges, especially in the relations between the sexes. "In my teens," said Frances, "I learned that a nice girl did not even start a conversation with a strange boy, and that as for anything more than conversation, my answer was to be a firm no."

Nearly every girl quickly gets the idea that it is her duty to prevent *physical* affection. She is to invite the pursuit of the male in a hundred ways. She is to be as desirable as possible, but always to be the keeper of propriety. It is a confusing game she plays. It is hard, thorough training which lasts perhaps ten years before marriage. Though she may give way in small matters or large, she is made to feel guilt in doing so. Her behavior is re-inforced by religion, custom and taboo. It is not surprising that slipping a wedding ring on her finger is not enough to change her deeply ingrained habit of rejection.

Examining attitudes toward sexual behavior in the codes of many societies, Ford and Beach reached this generally accepted conclusion: "The societies . . . that enjoin girls to be modest, retiring and submissive appear to produce adult women that are incapable or at least unwilling to be sexually aggressive. The feminine products of such cultural training are likely to remain relatively inactive during marital intercourse. And quite often, they do not experience clear-cut orgasm. In contrast, the so-cieties which permit or encourage early sex play usually allow women a greater degree of freedom in seeking sexual contacts. Under such circumstances the sexual performance of the mature woman seems to be characterized by a certain degree of aggres-sion, to include definite and vigorous activity, and to result reg-ularly in complete and satisfactory orgasm."

Ford and Beach do not advocate abandoning all our sexual customs. They merely state the problem, an attitude which is the handmaiden of most feminine problems in marital sex.

The woman who holds this attitude has long been conditioned to see herself in romantic but unphysical terms when it comes to sexual matters. As Virginia Johnson, Dr. Masters' assistant, puts it, "This is a female who has not ever considered herself, under socially acceptable circumstances, as a sexual being. (I don't mean involving herself overtly, but just thinking of herself as being permitted to anticipate the sexuality in her life or perhaps herself for it.) She has . . . put aside, once-removed, sexual feel-ings."

Marriage gives this woman permission to perceive sexually, adds Mrs. Johnson. But the change is not easy to make. Sexually "she is really not there . . . She is never really thinking and feeling in a sexual way."

In one sense, this woman has rejected part of her role as a female. And this rejection feeds upon a common resentment which most American women feel to some extent, a resentment which leads them to put aside the feminine role in other ways. Each of these rejections reinforces the other and confirms the feeling that being a woman is undesirable.

This second attitude appeared quickly in Frances Palmer's history. "I had just as good an education as Alan," she said, "at the same college. I worked just as hard, and some of my grades were better. But we married right out of school, and in three months I was pregnant. I had to quit my job, while Alan went right on using his education, growing, learning things and meeting people. I stayed home and changed diapers and fought dirt and watched my mind grow narrower.

"If you can accept that difference between the sexes," she added, "the physical sex difference isn't so hard to take. I liked the intimacy. But the romantic raptures never came. Alan didn't know how to bring them out. I found out that, for women, it was just another one of those differences, and I began to hate it while I still kept wanting it."

In our society, it is hard to find many women who do not in some ways share Frances Palmer's attitudes. For forces have been at work for centuries which tend to make the feminine role dissatisfying in some ways. In recent years these forces have accelerated to create tremendous pressure.

It is interesting to note a portrait of American women in the 1930s, written by novelist Pearl S. Buck, returning home after many years in China: "I observed frustration in the American woman. She often denied her frustration, insisting that she wanted to be married, that nobody had forced marriage on her, that it was woman's highest calling, her natural place, and so forth. Nevertheless . . . it was obvious that she was discontented in at least part of her being and most of the time. Her life was hectic . . . her time schedule not her own but that of her husband and children. . . . The American woman served her family as a duty, brightened by love, it is true . . . but the atmosphere she created in so doing was not one of continued content."

The portrait might suit today's American woman just as well. What made her unhappy with her role?

Sociologists agree it began centuries ago, with the rise of higher civilizations. The woman, who had been food gatherer, clothing maker, family doctor and many other things, was gradually replaced by others. The weaver began to weave the cloth, the farmer to grow the food.

Such changes were gradual, however, and the feminine social role was basically little altered until the industrial revolution. Now a machine did the work of many men, and the cost of manufactured goods plummeted. At the same time, using machines a man could now make more and thus earn more. With more money and cheaper prices, women could buy much that they formerly had made.

With greater wealth came greater leisure and education. Society could afford to educate even the females, who then began to seek rights to vote, to own and manage property, to move freely where and as they chose. But our cultural heritage links responsibilities to rights. As women became educated and free, there was automatic social pressure on them to play an active role in the world of money and affairs.

Today's woman faces a perplexity about her place in life. Many of her ancient duties have been assumed by industry, which provides no-iron shirts, baby foods in cans, frozen dinners and machines to wash and dry. Women have time, and they begin to feel insufficiently challenged by their classic role at the hearth.

And they are urged to dissatisfaction. Typical of the many calls to arms is this by anthropologist Margaret Mead: "Why have we returned, for all our great advances in technology, to the Stone Age arrangement in which woman's main ambition is to acquire and hold a mate, to produce or adopt children . . . and in which work outside the home . . . holds no attraction in itself. . . . The woman who does not marry is frowned upon. . . . Interest in any kind of work which might take precedence over the desire to have a family is discouraged."

Dr. Mead's call to discontent is echoed by the federal government, though for financial reasons, as a spur to the economy. Some agencies, such as the Atomic Energy Commission, have set up programs to entice women from the family to the office. At first, these recruits are given five-day part-time work. Then, in from six months to five years, they are gradually worked into full-time posts.

The response to such appeals is great. For one thing, while family income has increased about one and one-half times since World War II, debt has skyrocketed some *eighteen* times. Families need the money. Drawn by temptation on one hand and by pressure to get out of the home and do something "useful" on the other, women go to work. Today over 40 percent of America's work force is female, with more than two-thirds of them working at full-time jobs. By 1970 two of every five American women is expected to be working full-time.

One result is that the Department of Health, Education and Welfare reports there are now a million "latchkey" children who fend for themselves while mothers work. In 1966 the Office of Economic Opportunity spent $70 million to provide day care for such children so that mothers might hold jobs.

Though the average working woman is now forty years old or

more, there is a rapid lowering of this age. Forty percent of women work during the first year of marriage, and by the third year, 30 percent are still employed. A third of all women who work have youngsters under eighteen. Two and one-half million women on the job have children under six. The average young American girl can now look forward to twenty-five years of employment before she dies.

Nevertheless, most women who work do not necessarily resolve their conflict of career-versus-family, for they make only a half-hearted commitment. Educationally, though women comprise 30 percent of our college graduates, they get only 10 percent of the doctoral degrees. Mary Dublin Keyserling, director of the Women's Bureau of the U.S. Department of Labor reports: "Women are still concentrated in the same low-paying jobs they have traditionally held. In fact, they are becoming somewhat more concentrated in the relatively less skilled, less rewarded and less rewarding fields of work."

About 30 percent of women who work are in clerical jobs, 25 percent in service occupations and 15 percent in semiskilled factory work. They make up 80 percent of workers in apparel factories, nearly 45 percent in textile mills, and 90 percent of nurses, stenographers, typists and librarians.

When women do enter professional fields, 80 percent of them go into just six areas—teaching, nursing, social work, accounting, auditing and library science. In other words, contrary to much popular belief, women at work do not lose their traditional positions of personal service and subservience. They are rarely decision makers. Men remain their supervisors and employers. The housewife hires a baby-sitter, marches off to work, and then watches her male boss go off to an expense-account lunch while she eats a sandwich and answers the phone. Small wonder if she continues to resent her sexual identity. Woman remains the apparent inferior. The difference between the sexes confronts her starkly.

The important change is that she is no longer permitted to accept her ancient role as keeper of the hearth, binder of wounds, bearer and teacher and nurturer of the race. Instead of being allowed to glory in this role, she is taught to despise it as insufficient, as a biological aspect of her existence which interferes with her destiny. Where once she found her pride and fulfillment, now she finds only her chains. But if she sees them as such, and despises them as such, what she really begins to despise is the physical fact of being a woman.

Not all our no-iron apparel and instant food can change this simple fact. And not all of the technique we know can prevent sexual failure in the woman who hates being a woman. Nowhere is her rejection of her role more vivid than in her bedroom, for nowhere does her success demand that she be more essentially female.

This should not be construed as an appeal to return to a time past. That is neither possible nor desirable. But the fact is that in certain undeniably biological aspects of her life, to perform well, as well as she herself wants to perform, she must not deny what she unalterably is—a woman. For in this role she is better than an equal: she is herself. Whatever else she may be in other circumstances, in the marriage bed she must accept and reveal her essential identity.

How does she find that identity? Mainly, most marriage counselors find, simply by earnestly seeking it. And curiously, those counselors who have been able to deal rapidly with sexual difficulties report that when a woman understands the common barrier of role-denial, and when through physical means she is enabled to reach sexual fulfillment, she has often resolved her perplexity. For, whatever else she does in life, she now has a path to return to her femininity, a way to be what she is most essentially—to be, with delight, a woman.

9

---

of anger,
fear and love

ODERN psychiatry is coming to believe that most women who are blocked from sexual fulfillment by their emotions do not necessarily need long, deep therapy to be released. In fact, it is now known that even profound disturbance does not always prevent normal sexual satisfaction.

For example, the extreme case of frigidity is assumed by most psychiatrists to be the female homosexual. But when forty frankly homosexual women were studied, even the majority of these appeared to be capable of normal sexual experience with men.

Often in marital sex problems the block is not deeply hidden, requiring years to uncover and remove it. Instead, the source of the trouble often lies close to the surface. In many cases, it may not even be so much within the psyche of the individual as it is within the marriage itself, or within the circumstances of her life.

In psychotherapy, the essence of the treatment is to guide the patient to the discovery and understanding of her problem. When that problem is more easily found and recognized, the treatment can succeed rather quickly.

Thus, many doctors have come to think that sexual problems often need not be the province of the psychiatrist but may be dealt with by the family physician. Among those who hold this view are Dr. Terence McGuire and Dr. Richard Steinhilber, who advocate trying the simplest sort of approach to sexual difficulties before referring the patient to psychiatric help, and with the expectation of success, McGuire and Steinhilber advise family doctors to look for three basic reasons for a woman's sexual failure—reasons of anger, fear and love.

The case of Kay Barret shows how anger can become a barrier. She and her husband had quarreled to the point of divorce over her desire to work, and they finally asked the help of a marriage counselor. "Any baby-sitter," she said, "can be there when the children get home from school, give them something to eat and send them off to play. But Dick says the kids need me. He also says that with the extra expense of my working, and the higher taxes, I would add very little to our income. But money isn't the point. I feel a need to be more than a housekeeper."

At first Kay's plight seemed only an example of the social dilemma of modern women. But, suspecting more, the counselor probed her early life.

Kay's father was mild and acquiescent, her mother strong and aggressive. For example, her father had repeatedly refused to open his own business, despite her mother's urging. Kay's mother spent much time making and managing small real-estate investments, which became the family's only savings.

Kay soon learned that accomplishment was the way to her mother's heart. She got most affection when she made good grades, became a soloist in the church choir, was elected editor of her college yearbook.

Her college interest in boys was discouraged. "You'll have your fill of all that once you're married," her mother told her. "I had a chance to be something before I married, and I lost it once you were born. Don't be a fool."

Nevertheless, Kay fell in love with Dick in her senior year and wanted to marry. Her mother was firmly opposed and persuaded Kay to agree to wait a year. Graduating, Kay got a trainee's job in a department store and had a chance of becoming assistant buyer. But as her engagement to Dick lengthened, the sexual pressure grew. They spent some weekends together, and Kay became pregnant.

The sex had been unsatisfying, which the counselor attributed partly to guilt, a factor which helps make most premarital sex relations unsuccessful and often sets the stage for lifelong failure. Kay never reached orgasm after marriage either, though she responded sexually in all other ways. She gained relief through Dick's manual stimulation. For a day following intimacy she was irritable, and often she seemed to bait Dick into quarrels, chiefly about her wish to find a job.

Kay told the counselor that she still felt guilty about her premarital pregnancy, and the counselor felt sure that this guilt was because the pregnancy had cut off Kay's chance of achieving a career. In this way, she had lost her primary way of winning her mother's esteem, and her own self-esteem as well.

Kay also said that her mother frequently brought up the pregnancy in conversation, and repeatedly told Kay she was "too intelligent and well educated to waste [her] life as a glorified maid."

People do not carry guilt well. Often they handle it by shifting the blame and anger from themselves to someone else. Dick had become the scapegoat. Kay took the attitude that it was he who had insisted on the disastrous weekends and who now kept her from taking a job.

But actually, Dick told the counselor, he did not flatly oppose Kay's working. He simply thought it was a poor idea, and said so candidly. He added that Kay had made a number of plans to

approach employers and agencies, and had even set a few ap-
pointments. But when the time came, there was always a last-
minute reason why she could not go. Usually her reasons involved
something she had to do for Dick, mend or launder his clothes
or cook dinner for a business prospect. Each such episode seemed
to make Kay more hostile to Dick.

This anger was often revealed in the marriage bed. For Kay,
surrendering to her own feelings meant surrendering in a sense
to Dick, and this meant accepting a role as wife and mother
which made her feel guilt. Sexual satisfaction remained forbidden
fruit. She could desire it, and taste it, but never give way enough
to enjoy it fully. She said she felt little sensation once intercourse
began, though she had become very deeply aroused.

From a medical point of view Kay was normal. Her pelvic
muscles had fair tone. She was given exercise to improve the
tone, in the hope of making her aware of vaginal sensation.

But the counselor felt that Kay did not really *want* to have such
sensation. That would mean giving in to the wife-mother role.
Now each sexual failure denied that role. And the easy male
satisfaction at the same time heightened her resentment of the
role, setting the stage for the next failure.

The treatment of her case was quite simple since she was not
very deeply disturbed. The counselor merely rehearsed the facts
with her. He helped her confront the fact that Dick would not
really stand in the way of a career, the fact that Dick had not
been the only one who wanted the premarital intimacy, the fact
that she contrived excuses for not seeking jobs, and that in truth
she enjoyed caring for her home, her husband and her children.

None of this, of course, dealt with Kay's basic insecurity as the
daughter of a woman whose love had been in many ways neurotic,
who used her children as ways to overcome vicariously her own
frustrated ambitions and who largely disliked the role of a

woman. But it did help Kay to see that she was different from her mother, that her needs were not the same. As Kay's anger with herself and her husband weakened, her new understanding of the physical side of sex helped her cross the barrier to satisfaction. The new flush of womanly feeling reinforced her basic pleasure in being a wife and mother and made certain her sense of feminine identity.

Kay still felt the need to achieve. But now she was looking at some new avenues. Twice a week she helped out at a neighborhood school for retarded children, staffed mainly by volunteers. "Mother says," she told the counselor, "that it's typical woman's work, thankless drudgery. But it's satisfying work for me."

Marital anger as a bar to sexual fulfillment can take many forms. McGuire and Steinhilber find the most common are general resentment of men, envy of the masculine role as more privileged than the feminine, dislike of the partner, or resentment toward being dependent on him. Usually one of these hostilities leads to some of the others.

It is a rare marriage into which some kind of anger has not entered. When the woman fails sexually, some anger toward her husband is certain. For she is likely to feel that he has failed her as a lover. As one marriage counselor puts it: "A woman won't blame her husband because he is not the world's best engineer or athlete, or because he is not rich or witty. But in love, she tends to demand perfection. Her life is built around love. When its physical reality fails, she is hurt and puzzled, mistrusts herself and her marriage. Often she decides that the flaw lies in her husband's ability as a lover.

"But physically, how good a lover can he be? If he feels affection and expresses it gently, if he is physically able to have intercourse, if he is responsive to his wife's reactions, what more can he do? A satisfying sexual relationship ought to ensue. If it does not, we must look for reasons why the woman does not fully respond to him."

It is hard for two people to live closely without some hostility arising. One important source of such anger is the fact that most sexual relationships begin with orgasmic failure for the woman. And if there is any other anger, it is reinforced by this frustration and disappointment in sex. Blame and resentment are easily bred. And failure thus may become self-perpetuating. For every time the sex act begins, anger stirs, as the conditioned expectation of a frustrating experience rises.

This is why counselors who talk with women about to be married caution them that they are not likely to reach satisfaction at first and try to explain why the fault will not be that of either partner—that satisfying intercourse must be learned. With no frustrated expectation, and no blame, good adjustment is much more likely to be achieved in the long run. Without such a warning, an expectation built up during the courtship is usually doomed to a bitter ending on the honeymoon. With this may come grave doubts that the girl has chosen the right man. If they were really so much in love, and really adequate, the couple are likely to feel, where are the thunder and lightning that novels have led them to expect?

Most counselors focus on an expectation of pleasure from the first physical intimacy, a delight in the closeness, with the gradual learning of satisfaction. For they know that once disappointment has been allowed to yield anger, a massive barrier to sexual fulfillment has been raised.

No less a bar to satisfied love than anger is fear. And the case of Lynn Burke illustrates the phenomenon well.

Lynn's religion forbade contraception. And Lynn feared motherhood. Lynn was the eldest of seven children. After the birth of the last, Lynn's mother developed a tumor which required the removal of the womb, and Lynn remembered that her mother seemed very relieved.

As the eldest, Lynn was her mother's assistant and confidante. The mother spoke freely about a number of minor chronic illnesses with which childbirth had left her and about "the pain of giving birth." She was not a strong woman, and she died of a heart attack soon after Lynn's marriage. Lynn believed her mother's heart had been weakened by childbearing and by the work of rearing a large family.

Perhaps because of the common inclination to approach the things we fear most, Lynn was permissive with boys. She had a series of steady dates and petted with all of them. Affectionate, she enjoyed the experiences. By the end of high school, though she had not had intercourse, she was experienced in many ways. She had learned to forestall intercourse, when pressured, by initiating a more permissive petting which ended in orgasm.

In courtship, Lynn used the same technique with John. Their engagement lasted two years. Lynn repeatedly delayed marriage, using money as the reason. She said she did not want the hand-to-mouth existence her mother had known. She wanted a bank account.

Though the physical intimacy in courtship had created intense feeling for both, with marriage there was bitter physical failure. When entry was attempted, Lynn felt only pain, and intromission did not occur. The couple believed entrance had been prevented by the hymen, the tissue which partly closes the entrance to the vagina in virginity.

Contrary to common belief, the hymen is usually merely stretched, though it may tear slightly in some cases, producing a few drops of blood. Discomfort at first intercourse, when it occurs, is usually the result of stretching this and other tissues. Normally, as repeated effort is made to enter the vagina, the hymen gradually stretches out of the way and recedes. Occasionally a doctor may feel it is wisest to nick the hymen with a surgical scalpel to facilitate stretching. But in the main this is unnecessary.

Lynn asked her doctor to help her in opening the hymen. But he found that the tissue could not possibly have caused the pain and sense of obstruction she described. The hymen had already been widely stretched by Lynn's many petty episodes. He concluded that the pain and blocked entry were due to what is known as *vaginismus*.

This is a spasm of the muscles at the *introitus*, the entrance of the vagina. These external muscles form a ringlike rim, and when tensed can easily resist the male organ. Almost invariably a spasm of the muscles is psychologically caused, sometimes merely by the usual bridal tension, exaggerated by a little extra fear. The doctor began by explaining the situation to Lynn and urging her to relax.

In a few weeks Lynn did overcome tension enough to permit entry. But then she felt no vaginal sensation to speak of, though she became extremely moved, as always, by the preliminary affection.

Lynn avoided pregnancy by the only means her religion allowed—the "rhythm method," avoiding intercourse when conception was most likely. But like many women, Lynn's menstrual cycle was not dependable. Within four months, she was pregnant.

The pregnancy was uncomfortable, with much nausea, attributable in part to her fear. And birth was difficult, with Lynn's tense apprehension adding to the trouble. A year later she saw a marriage counselor. She and John were fighting about having more children.

Lynn refused to have another child for several years, even threatening to defy the Church and use contraceptive pills. When John objected, she said she would deny him intercourse entirely, adding that she got little pleasure from it anyway.

The counselor felt that fear of childbirth was only one element of Lynn's problem. The woman who wants caresses and stimulation, but not intercourse, is familiar in psychological cases.

Lynn complained that John would spend hours making love to her before marriage but that now he wanted to proceed to intercourse after twenty or thirty minutes of affection. The counselor explained that this was quite normal. And he knew that such complaints are often the sign of sexual immaturity, a continuing rejection of the mature act.

"It's almost," John told the counselor, "as if Lynn wanted to go on being a girl, doing something forbidden, instead of a married woman."

The counselor felt John's intuition was good, and he tried to learn from Lynn why this might be so. Asking about her parents, he learned that her father tended to run away from family problems, leaving them to her mother, joining endless clubs and committees. "He always had a meeting somewhere," said Lynn, "and he wouldn't be back till late. He wasn't drinking or anything, just staying out of the problems. Mother learned to do the things a man should do, and I helped her. We worked in the yard and fixed things that broke. Once we even cut up a small tree that fell."

The counselor realized that childbirth was a symbol of the dependence Lynn feared, as well as a fear on its own. What she was most afraid of was to be left alone with a house full of children. She said she wanted to go back to work as soon as her first child was in school.

The counselor asked why, and Lynn said that, though John made good money, she wanted a bank account of her own. She also said she wanted to keep up skills to fall back on—just in case.

One problem in this case was that John was a man of very few words, and Lynn needed reassurance. The counselor persuaded

John to verbalize his strong feelings of responsibility toward Lynn and their child, to say what he had always thought, that whatever he earned belonged to Lynn as much as to him. As soon as he did so, Lynn began to confide some of her fears to him, and the new communication gave Lynn far more confidence in her husband.

Lynn was also reassured by getting better information about the rhythm method of contraception. She realized that she had conceived the first time by depending too heavily on an exact twenty-eight-day menstrual cycle, which she did not follow. She had also not known that sperm were capable of fertilization for a day or two after intercourse.

More sure of John and of their ability to control the size of their family without total abstinence, Lynn was now able to seek satisfaction in intercourse. With some guidance from her doctor, she achieved coital orgasm in a few weeks. Her feelings of maturity and feminine identity were strengthened, helping to relieve her deep-seated insecurity.

Fear of pregnancy is perhaps the most common of fear barriers to sexual fulfillment. But it is usually related to anxiety about becoming subjugated to the male (especially when the woman has seen an instance of male exploitation), about helpless dependency, about growing up and becoming a woman.

There may be fear of intercourse itself—the anxiety that it will be painful, disgusting or will fail. Such fears, for obvious reasons, tend to be self-realizing. So do most other fears. (Lynn's behavior was beginning to drive her husband away from home and produce just the situation of which she was afraid.)

But while fears may bar sexual release, often if satisfaction can be realized, the anxieties are allayed. Where once it was believed that only the emotionally mature could experience sexual completion, it is now being found that mature sexual response can be achieved first and that the resulting confidence and sense of identity can support the maturing of the whole personality.

As overt a barrier as fear may be, so can the barrier of love be extremely subtle. In such cases, attachment to someone other than the husband makes it difficult for the woman to give herself completely to the sexual experience. She holds something back and thus denies her own pleasure.

Family attachment is typical of such a barrier. Emily Harwood's mother was a widow with a large home; she said it was foolish for Emily and Jim to rent an apartment when they married.

Jim did not like the idea, but Emily persisted, saying that in this way her mother could gradually get used to the prospect of being alone. Meanwhile, the couple could save enough on rent to think of buying their own house. Jim finally gave in.

But Emily tended to remain a little girl in her mother's home. It seemed pointless to cook, clean, launder and take meals separately, so Emily and her mother did these things together. And the mother ended by doing most of the planning and decision making, as she had always done.

Emily's mother had been unsatisfied by sex and a little repelled by it. She had conveyed these feelings to her daughter to some extent, and had always discouraged Emily from the most harmless sort of physical affection with young men.

Jim had gradually overcome Emily's reticence during courtship, and by the time they married she was aroused and anticipating. But in her mother's house she felt guilt whenever Jim approached her. She felt her mother might hear any smallest sound they made. Rather than concentrate her attention on her own sensations, she listened anxiously. She became afraid that her mother would know if she had intercourse and began to avoid any opportunity. She never went to bed early or rose late. She was careful not to be alone with Jim in their room during the day. The situation grew worse as Emily's anxiety fed upon itself.

Jim insisted they find an apartment of their own. They fought, and Emily kept winning delays. She said her mother might think they had been unhappy in the house. The quarrels increased in number and intensity until they sought the help of a marriage counselor.

Taking the traditional view, the counselor might have thought that Emily needed long psychotherapy to ferret out the roots of what appeared to be a complex overdependence on her mother, with a fixation at an adolescent stage of emotional development. Traditionally, too, the physician who examined and interviewed Emily might have diagnosed deep psychoneurosis from the physical symptoms she related. In recent months, she told the doctor, her digestion had seemed upset at bedtime. She had a great many headaches, with nausea. When she did have intercourse, she was sleepless afterward, her eyes burned and she had an ache in her lower back which lasted into the next day. Her menstrual periods, which had been fairly normal, now brought great discomfort.

Such a cluster of symptoms is typical of the psychosomatic complaints of neurotics, real enough distress caused by the emotions. Such symptoms are also very commonly present in women who do not achieve orgasm in intercourse. This is one reason why it was concluded that all women who failed sexually were psychoneurotic.

Here we have a chicken-and-egg situation. For it now seems quite well accepted that sexual failure will produce neurosis of a kind, just as surely as neurosis can produce sexual failure. The puzzle can become subtle indeed. For example, sexual arousal without release can leave the sex organs in an advanced state of congestion for hours afterward. Even the womb increases greatly in size. With orgasm, this congestion may be almost gone in ten minutes. Repeated frustration is thought to set the stage for real physical damage. Says Dr. Thomas Myers, "When she is repeatedly . . . confronted with an aroused expectancy of attaining orgasm, which is frustrated, actual pathology of the tissues results."

The question for the therapist is: Where to enter this vicious circle? The successful rapid treatment of sexual problems has been achieved through a direct seeking after sexual adjustment, while trying to deal quickly with the emotional difficulties which are close to the surface.

In Emily's case, she was persuaded to find a furnished apartment at once. Meanwhile she was given exercises and sex information. The apartment forced her to take up the responsibilities of a woman, and also immediately reduced some of the tension involved in her sexual relationship with her husband. She and Jim were counseled not to expect sexual perfection at once but to enjoy the pleasure of each moment of intimacy for its own sake. This advice removed from both much of the pressure to perform. In about two months Emily reached orgasm.

This approach to sex difficulty comes under the psychiatric heading of "behavior therapy." One of the leading behavior therapists, Dr. Joseph Wolpe of Temple University Medical School, sees neurotic disorders as "anxiety reactions." These are anxious responses to matters which do not make the normal person anxious; for example, being introduced to someone, or looking out the window of a tall building. Wolpe and others believe that the sex act can become such an anxiety producer, with resulting failure of orgasm.

Behavior therapy may try to attenuate the anxiety of a situation without insistence on uncovering its roots with long analysis. In sexual difficulties the attempt now is often to use the new physical understanding to heighten sexual excitement so that it can overcome anxiety, especially that anxiety which is not the result of deep neurosis.

Masters and Johnson apply this method to couples who come to them for a two-week course of intensive treatment. And it works. At the American Institute of Family Relations, women are being placed in sex discussion groups led by a counselor, who conveys the newer sex information and then leads the women in discussing the knowledge in terms of their own experience. At the same time, the group members are examined for muscular weakness and taught to exercise the P.C. by a physician specialist. "Our rate of success is so good," says one institute counselor working in the program, "that we are now actually hunting hard for failures, in order to make scientific reports of the project more believable. We are succeeding in just about every case."

It would seem that the most common forms of psychological blockage of sexual response can be broken through by the simplest insights combined with physical enhancement.

One important advantage of this approach is that it can prevent a whole chain of difficulties; once sexual failure has marred a marriage, it becomes entangled in a bewildering web of emotion. Consider the typical honeymoon. The woman is expectant. During courtship she has probably been aroused repeatedly, including attempts at intercourse, without completion. The wedding preparations and excitement have left her psychically overwrought and exhausted. Poor information gives her only the vaguest idea of her role in physical love. She believes that, fully in love, she should respond automatically and overwhelmingly. This is the culmination for which she has waited. After years of saying no, she now surrenders to her love.

In such circumstances, vaginal orgasm is a rare occurrence. If the woman is a virgin, it is even rarer because of some likely discomfort attendant on the stretching of the hymen.

At once the web has begun. Perhaps, she fears, this was not the great love she had supposed. Perhaps she is less than a woman, is really cold at heart. Perhaps it is her husband's lack of consideration, his selfishness. It is plain to her that he had *his* pleasure. She felt aroused. And his doubts become the mirror of hers, doubts of himself as a man, of her as a woman, of the marriage as the union he had hoped for.

With the release of restraints, desire and physical curiosity are keen in the honeymoon, despite this first disappointment. And there is the normal reaction of trying harder to overcome failure. Already there is an element of pressure-to-perform for both. They become self-conscious and anxious, almost insuring that they will fail. With each failure, doubt and resentment grow. The lack of physical release may also increase the woman's irritability, both physically and emotionally.

"What is surprising," says one psychologist, "is that more than a handful of couples survive the honeymoon without divorce."

From this disturbing emotional brew, other latent problems gather strength—fears of marriage, fears of dependency, fears of parenthood, resentments of the feminine role. There may be a heightening of a tendency to retreat, to regress to adolescent or childish behavior and to reject maturity, thus strengthening some of the sexual barriers of family attachment. By the time the couple might reach help—and very few ever do—it is not easy for the most sophisticated therapist to untangle the web.

Casting about for explanations of their disappointment, the couple introduce endless false leads. Small, unimportant fears may be drawn from memory, a homosexual experience in early adolescence, episodes of masturbation, feelings of sexual attraction to unlikely people, recurring dreams, resentments of the opposite sex or of the role of one's own sex, depressions, losses, illnesses. Any one of these leads might be significant. Yet any one might only be part of the vicissitudes of normal maturation. Both partners are very likely to present psychosomatic complaints, a picture of depression and irritability, signs of a wish to escape, fantasy solutions to their problems. Remember that most of the symptoms of emotional disturbance are only exaggerations of normal feelings and thoughts. What is really wrong in these individuals and this marriage?

When the couple tries to unwind this skein after years of marriage and partial or complete sexual failure, it is not easy. Defenses have been built up. Self-blame and self-doubt may well have led to doubt and blame of the partner. Adultery may have been resorted to, as a proof of adequacy. The emotional lure has been tarnished for the couple; physical familiarity has dulled some of the early excitement.

Thus, one of the first essentials is to relieve mutual blame and doubt and secure a fresh beginning. And so frequently is ignorance of sexual function the basic villain that most of the time it is safe to begin here. Generally there is enough basic affection and emotional maturity to make sexual satisfaction possible. And with that satisfaction, many old wounds simply vanish. Most couples who achieve a fulfilling sexual relationship where there has been none before report more than sensual pleasure; they are likely to say that every other aspect of marriage has improved.

As Havelock Ellis pointed out, after a discussion of the psychological study of sex: "But sex is first of all a physical fact, and the relationship of sex is primarily and fundamentally a physical relationship."

It is not surprising that, although no marriage is without its anger and fear and doubt, physical guidance can bring physical fruition to the sex act. We have examined all but one phase of this guidance as it applies to the woman who fails to respond fully to physical love, and that is the physical failure of her partner.

We do not refer here to true impotence, the inability of the male to become erect enough to enter the woman in intercourse. This is almost always the result of rather deep emotional disturbance or severe physical debility. It is rare except in old age, and is the province of the psychiatrist or the urologist. Little can be achieved by discussing the problem here.

On the other hand, there is a common male factor which can work physical and emotional havoc on the sexual relationship, a factor so common that to some extent it may bar sexual adjustment in a majority of marriages. Little discussed, rarely admitted by the men it troubles, it can make meaningless all the physical and psychological help given to women and make feminine sexual failure a certainty. Once considered a difficult matter, it is now treated in most cases with rapid success.

10

---

the
bitter quickness

It was Betty Caxton's tenth visit to the marriage counselor, and her sexual failure was unyielding. Yet there seemed to be no physical reason and no important lack of information, nor any barrier of the emotions which was insuperable.

The counselor reviewed the details of the relationship once more. Then he asked the neglected question, and the key to the Caxtons' difficulty became clear. "How long," he inquired, "does actual intercourse last?"

Betty Caxton said she thought the time was probably normal but that she could not estimate it in minutes. "Look at the second hand of your watch," suggested the counselor. "Watch how long it takes for the second hand to make a sweep of one minute."

Betty complied. "It isn't at all that long," she said.

The counselor had the probable answer, and he blamed himself for overlooking the obvious. For according to Kinsey and others, the average woman reaches orgasm only after five minutes of intercourse, with some 12 percent needing ten minutes.

On the other hand, Kinsey found the average male reached orgasm in less than two minutes, with 75 percent of men in this category. Large numbers of men completed the act in less than a minute.

Successful intercourse, in another study, seemed to last between three and five minutes on the average. But whatever the precise figures, it is well known that if the typical man simply pursued his own climax, he would reach it before the typical woman was ready for hers. In other words, without some means of slowing the response of the male, successful intercourse is likely to be difficult.

(Speeding the woman's reaction would seem to be an alternative. But in practical terms, it is widely accepted that this cannot be done enough to compensate for the uncontrolled male's speed of reaction.)

Obviously, this sex difference becomes a firm barrier to the satisfaction of many women. But happily the barrier can be raised.

The bitter quickness of men is known to doctors as premature ejaculation. This term is as vaguely and inaccurately used as is the word frigidity. It is certainly applied fairly to those men who ejaculate immediately on entering the vagina or even before. But broadly speaking, premature ejaculation describes the failure of a man who reaches orgasm before his wife is satisfied. Plainly, with a woman who does not respond orgasmically to any amount of intercourse, as is the case of the many women who receive little or no stimulation from the presence of the male organ in the vagina, this definition does not work. One must presuppose that the female partner is responsive to intercourse. And from all studies it would appear that if she will reach climax in intercourse at all, she will most probably do so in no more than ten minutes of coitus, though this would be unusually long. However, it suggests the length of time which is reasonably asked of the man.

A very large number of men cannot sustain intercourse so long. Says Dr. Frederic Damrau, one of the leading authorities in the field: "Feminine frigidity due to frustration is a common result of premature ejaculation." Without supplying exact numbers, Dr. Damrau suggests the size of the problem in saying, "In a considerable number, climax is reached within less than a minute, or even ten or twenty seconds after entrance."

Dr. Masters describes the common problem this way: "He is trying to delay this process. His wife, with her complete fear of his lack of success in the matter, is grabbing, thrusting, demanding, in order to achieve satisfaction before he ejaculates . . . Occasionally she is successful. Usually she is not, and he ejaculates."

Such quickness is bitter not only for women but for men as well. Not only is too quick an orgasm incompletely satisfying, but worse, the man feels impotent, inadequate to his wife's needs. For if he reaches orgasm more than a few seconds before she is ready, her increasing sexual tension is almost immediately broken. In any case, physically it is a very rare male who can sustain full erection for more than seconds after orgasm. The penis may remain somewhat enlarged, but it does not have the firmness needed to apply stimulating pressure to the walls of the vagina or to create the traction which is conveyed to the external feminine organs. (The woman with good vaginal musculature and control may sustain stimulation for a few seconds longer by exerting greater pressure with the P.C. muscle, but this maneuver rarely succeeds well enough.)

It is almost unknown for the average man to reach a second orgasm without losing his erection. And the erection is not likely to be recovered in less than half an hour to an hour after the first orgasm.

Curiously, most couples seem to accept the briefness of intercourse with little question, though not, especially among women, without envy and resentment. It is an obvious statement of men's sexual advantage and a likely source of dissatisfaction with the feminine role.

And few men seek help for this weakness. They may accept it as a normal matter or even as a sign of potency. More often, however, they feel inadequate and want to conceal the fact.

The problem has been discussed for many centuries, and until recently the answer went unchanged. It was for the man to distract himself, and thus try to reduce the sexual tension which moved him inexorably toward climax. He has been advised to do everything from mentally reciting verses to worrying about his business problems.

India of the twelfth century at least had more poetic suggestions, as the *Koka Shastra* indicates: "Men normally attain orgasm more quickly than women. Knowing this, the man must so handle the woman that she is thoroughly moist beforehand . . .

"However passionate he may be, a man can remain indefinitely potent if during intercourse he directs his thoughts to woods, rivers, caves, mountains or other pleasant places, and proceeds gently and slowly. If he imagines a particularly nimble monkey swinging on the branch of a tree, he will not ejaculate. . . ."

Such diversions are not very effective. And whether the subject be a monkey or the Dow-Jones averages, self-distraction seems inimical to an expression of love. It is also axiomatic that the brain does not manage two thoughts at the same time. The man who is busy trying not to notice the demanding sensations of intercourse certainly cannot be the man who is trying to perceive and respond to the subtleties of what is happening between male and female organs. He must be aware.

That male prematurity is controllable can be seen in other cultures. In the Marquesas Islands, men are trained in control from boyhood, and most can prolong erection almost indefinitely, can continue intercourse for an hour (though presumably not in anything like an active way) and permit ejaculation only at will.

Physically these men are no different from Americans in this potential.

But Dr. Charles Lloyd comments: "In many cultures, particularly Western, sexual know-how never reaches the expertise to permit good control."

To understand prematurity, it helps to know the function of the male organs involved (see Figure 18). In the testes, the twin egg-shaped organs which are suspended in a pouch behind the penis, there is continual manufacture of the male reproductive cells, the spermatazoa.

The sperm are moved from the testes through intricate pathways by tiny contractions of smooth muscle, muscle not under control of the will. They go into the *ductus deferens*, a long tube leading upward from the testes and into the body.

The *ductus deferens* makes a long loop, going around the urinary bladder. As this loop descends, it opens into a larger passage, called the ejaculatory duct. Where these two ducts meet, inside the body, is another sex organ, the seminal vesicle. This also opens into the ejaculatory duct. It produces a special fluid which bathes the sperm. These two secretions move along the ejaculatory duct until they enter the urethra, the urinary passage, which connects the bladder and the penis. In the urethra a third secretion is added. This third fluid is a kind of carrier, which makes up the bulk of the material ejaculated. It comes from the prostate gland, a large organ between the testes and the anus. When the fourth secretion is added to those in the urethra, from Cowper's glands, nearby, the semen has been assembled, each element having a role to play in reproduction. The assembly takes place as sexual excitement grows in the man.

As the man becomes stimulated sexually, his erection becomes maximal. At the same time, the testicles enlarge and rise to lie close against the body, instead of hanging loosely suspended. This change in position is thought, at least in part, to help provide a more forceful ejaculation. In some men, the rise of the left (usually the larger) testicle to its highest position is a signal that orgasm is close at hand.

The orgasm itself has similarities to the woman's. Increasing tension ends in a series of muscular contractions, the first two or three about four-fifths of a second apart, and those following at longer intervals. A number of muscles are involved, squeezing sharply on the passage which carries the ejaculatory secretions. Largest and strongest of these muscles is the P.C., which surrounds and supports the internal portion of the urethra. The semen is forced the length of the urethra and out of the penis. The first contractions can propel the semen twelve inches.

The entire penis is fairly responsive to the stimulation which yields orgasm, but three areas are most acutely sensitive (see Figure 19). One is the region of the glans, the bulbous cap of the penis. Maximum sensation is usually found just under the small cleft at the bottom of the glans. The next most sensitive is probably the area of the coronal ridge, the ridgelike prominence which encircles most of the glans. The third responsive area is the *corpus spongiosum*, the tubelike prominence which runs the length of the penis along the bottom of the organ. Within this prominence is the external portion of the urethra, the passage through which the ejaculatory fluid travels.

Stimulation of the penis sends nerve impulses to a sexual center in the spinal cord. At a peak of stimulation, a reflex action takes place in this center, and the muscles involved in orgasm are commanded to contract. This peak is not, of course, reached only by sensation in the penis. A wide variety of physical and psychological stimuli create sexual excitement. But in most men orgasm is not produced without direct stimulation of the penis.

Figure 18. The male reproductive system.

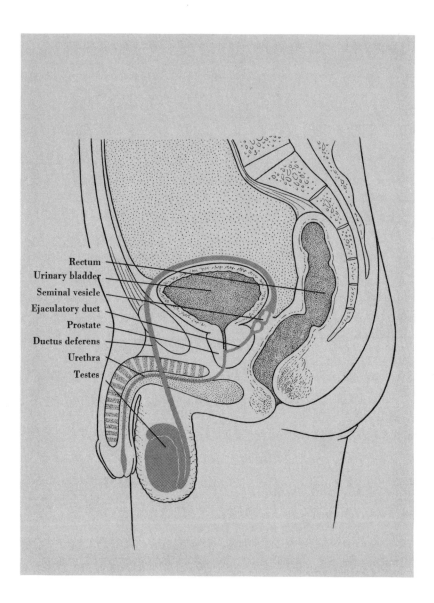

Rectum
Urinary bladder
Seminal vesicle
Ejaculatory duct
Prostate
Ductus deferens
Urethra
Testes

Figure 19. Penis in state of erection.

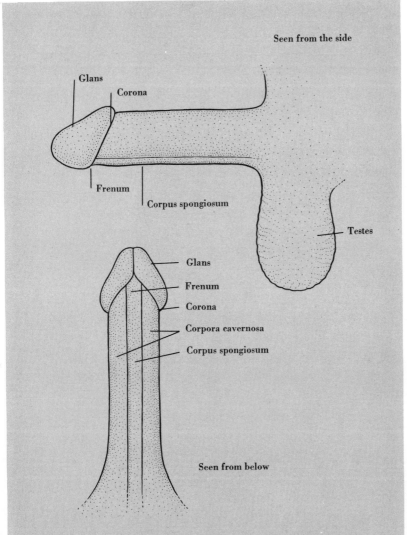

What can be done to slow down the reflex of ejaculation? Until recently most psychiatrists believed that quick ejaculation was a sign of emotional disturbance, often a hostility to women. But doctors now feel the problem is a complex of physical and emotional factors, which can be solved by simple training and understanding. Dr. Frederic Damrau expresses the authoritative view when he says, "My experience confirms the belief that any accompanying psychoneurosis is the result of premature ejaculation, rather than its cause."

The very vast majority of men, however, are not aware of how easily they can gain ejaculatory control. The truth is, few seek it. In one study of average California marriages, 40 percent of the men said they had *virtually no control* over orgasm. But only one man in five said he had made any attempt to gain control. Such attempts were usually of the rather ineffective self-distraction type.

Though there are physical paths to control, the roots of prematurity seem chiefly emotional. Typically, for Fred Caxton the quickness began on his wedding night. He and Betty were very young and without more than cursory sexual experience. Their year-long engagement had produced intense feeling and intense frustration. There had been petting, but without orgasm. Like many couples, the Caxtons reached marriage after a long build-up toward sexual release.

(The problem is often the same when there is premarital sex. In fact, it is likely to be worse, due to guilt, furtiveness and poor settings. Unsuccessful sex only heightens the tension for both, even though the man becomes orgasmic.)

The wedding was large and followed by an elaborate reception. The couple reached a hotel room nervous and tired. Sexual tension rose quickly, together with mutual fears about performing adequately since neither was well informed. No sooner had Fred made entrance than there was an uncontrollable orgasm.

Betty's tension and anxiety burst into anger. She had felt nothing but the discomfort of a stretching hymen. She reproached Fred, and he felt a keen sense of inadequacy. After an hour's quarrel, he tried again. Again he ejaculated at once.

With each intimacy Fred's anxiety grew. Since tension precipitates male orgasm, his reaction, if anything, quickened. No effort at control helped. He provided relief for his wife with manual stimulation, and the pattern of disappointment persisted.

Betty grew to accept transitory intercourse, Fred to accept a sense of inadequacy. With this reduced pressure and greater familiarity with intimacy, Fred could sustain intercourse for thirty seconds more.

At the marriage counselor's suggestion, Fred saw a urologist, a specialist in urinary and reproductive disorders of men. The doctor found no disease. Some doctors think certain conditions can speed up the reflex of orgasm. These are chiefly inflammations of the penis, the urethra, or the prostate, the gland which produces most of the seminal fluid. The inflammation is thought to augment sexual engorgement.

The doctor explained to Fred the typical vicious circle of premature ejaculation. Tension produces the prematurity. Each instance makes the man more tense for the next, and so on. In a sense, the doctor said, the need was to break a bad habit. Fred needed confidence.

Fred was skeptical. The overwhelming urge to orgasm, once intercourse began, seemed too overpowering to be controlled so simply, if at all.

The doctor explained to Betty how she could help. "Your understanding," he said, "will do much to solve the problem. While we work on this, you must never blame Fred for poor performance. You must help him to have confidence and to believe he is gaining control, for he will be."

The Caxtons were to try a simple approach to the problem at first, an adjustment of attitude and technique, which is all many couples need. The method is much like that recommended for the unresponding woman—with slow, gentle entrance, and no movement at first. Betty's improved muscular control would enable her to find more stimulation without overstimulating Fred, as she contracted the muscles of the vagina.

"Many couples," the doctor said, "think vigorous thrusting is the expected technique in intercourse, perhaps because this becomes the instinct as orgasm nears. But friction, while masking sensation for the woman, overstimulates the man.

"After entrance with no movement, he should remain motionless for a time. Then he can move very slowly, trying to stimulate the vaginal walls with as little friction to the penis as possible, pressing, rather than rubbing. Each moment intercourse can be sustained will add to Fred's confidence."

Through this technique, and with no criticism by either, Fred gradually lengthened the time he could remain in intromission. The same technique helped Betty to perceive and seek vaginal sensation. In a few months they had achieved mutual satisfaction.

Dr. Arnold Kegel poses another theory for the success of this method. He points out that stimulation to the male organ tends to be more frictional in a relaxed vagina. Improved musculature holds the penis more firmly and shifts sensation toward pressure, which is less likely to provoke a premature reflex. He finds that women who have improved this musculature report their husbands to be less premature. Some experts add a psychological element to Kegel's theory, saying that the better the chance of feminine satisfaction, the less the male fear of being too quick, of performing inadequately. "Nothing so relaxes a tense, premature male," says one doctor, "as a responsive, uncritical woman."

While this approach is helpful to all premature men, a great many need something more. In recent years many ideas have been tried.

Some doctors believe the speed of the reflex is simply quicker in some men. With this in mind, Dr. Robert L. Rowan, of New York's St. Vincent's Hospital, has prescribed tranquilizers, hoping to depress the ejaculatory center in the spine. But he adds that basically "Treatment consists of reassurance and adequate interest in the patient."

Another therapy, more widely used, is an anesthetic cream to dim the sensitivity of the penis so that fewer nerve impulses go to the spine. Dr. Frederic Damrau has given patients such a cream, which is put on perhaps a half hour before intercourse, then wiped off. Damrau finds the ejaculation is almost always slowed in this way. Use of the cream is stopped after five to thirty days, when longer intercourse has been achieved. Again it appears that once the man has had intercourse of normal duration his confidence in himself reduces the tension.

The largest study of premature ejaculation was made by Dr. Bernard Schapiro, formerly of the Magnus Hirschfeld Institute in Berlin. He reviewed 1,130 cases, many being his own patients.

Schapiro concluded that prematurity had no single cause, though he felt some of the men had greater sensitivity of the glans penis and he had prescribed anesthetic cream effectively. He, too, found that retraining, with the relief of pressure from blame and anxiety, was the answer. But he summed up that "Premature ejaculation can be explained neither on the basis of purely psychic nor of purely somatic [bodily] factors."

Most experts agree that the treatment of prematurity must take into account the physical as well as the emotional. Sound information on sexual technique and physiology is the obvious first step. And this alone reduces tension. But while a number of doctors have found success with anesthetic creams, tranquilizers, or sensation-reducing sheaths, these are not considered methods of choice. For they interpose a mechanical quality which experts feel may be a further emotional hazard.

Instead, therapists have developed training techniques to deal with prematurity in other ways. One such has been developed by Dr. James H. Semans of Duke University.

To break the old pattern of anxiety, doubt and tension, he first has patients refrain from intercourse for a time. He asks for the help of the wife and carefully teaches her the training technique.

Semans' method depends on a warning signal of impending male orgasm. This is greatly heightened tension and sensation around the glans, the penile cap. Once this intense sensation is pointed out to men, they can easily recognize it. During retraining, the sensation is a signal to stop stimulation of the penis. If stimulation is stopped promptly, as soon as the warning feeling arises, ejaculation is prevented and sexual tension can decline.

Intercourse is replaced by mutual manual stimulation by the couple. Thus the man is less profoundly stimulated, and stopping is simpler. At the same time, the stimulation of the wife can continue. The man signals when stimulation of the penis is to stop and to begin again. Orgasm is permitted the man only when the woman is also ready.

Semans finds that men can soon forestall ejaculation indefinitely in this manner. He then counsels a second step. The same system is used, but with a lubricating jelly on the penis to simulate more of the sensations of intercourse. When again ejaculation can be put off indefinitely, it can usually be controlled in intercourse. This point is usually reached in six to eight weeks.

Curiously, other cultures are known to use similar techniques.

In one society, it is used to train male children to such control. Psychologists warn this would be dangerous in our culture.

Using the same principles applied by Semans and others in this training, Masters recently told the American Fertility Society of a still more rapid method. This usually succeeds in two weeks. It uses a simple technique by which the wife can prevent her husband's ejaculation.

For the first seventy-two hours, the man learns the concept of control. This is done through manual stimulation by the woman. But just before the man reaches the stage Masters calls "ejaculatory inevitability," there is a different technique used by the woman.

When the man is in danger of ejaculating, the wife places a thumb and two fingers on the male organ. The thumb is positioned on the frenum—this is the point just below the cleft at the bottom of the glans penis, where there is a little gathering of loose tissue (see Figure 19). Then, opposite her thumb, she puts a finger on each side of the corona, the pronounced ridge which circles the cap of the penis. One finger is placed just behind the ridge, the other just ahead of it. With her fingers in these positions, she firmly, boldly squeezes them toward her thumb. This does not cause the man any pain, even when the squeeze is quite a strong one. Immediately, he loses the urge to ejaculate. Also, Masters says, his erection diminishes slightly, about 10 to 15 percent. She then begins manual stimulation again, waits until he nears ejaculation, and then squeezes once more. Now and then he may wait too long, and ejaculate. There is no harm in this, and the wife is warned to be uncritical, to let him rest, then begin excitation again, as before. "Within forty-eight hours," says Masters, "this male has a concept of the degree of excitation that he can achieve and maintain."

The next step is aimed at the man's sensitization to being inside the vagina. This alone is enough to trigger ejaculation within a short time in most men who are premature.

The man lies on his back. The woman straddles him from above, and he enters her. She moves far enough toward his chest so that the penis is not bent downward, but can rest within her in the normal, upward-slanting position of erection. Now she merely sits. When he reaches an excitation which he now knows to be the furthest safe approach to ejaculation, she rises, squeezes the male organ as before, and again he enters her. Masters reports that in three days the average male can remain in intromission, without any movement, of course, for some twenty minutes. He has now conquered his oversensitization to the vagina.

The couple now enters the third phase, in which the man enters in the least stressful of coital positions, facing the woman, with both lying on their sides. He remains still. But now she, gently, moves in what is described as a "nondemanding" way. In other words, she may seek some stimulation, but makes no strong effort to reach orgasm. She understands that her satisfactions will be minimal for about two weeks. Masters summarizes: "It takes the average male, ages twenty-five to fifty-five, some ten days to learn fifteen to twenty minutes of intravaginal containment with ejaculatory control during the female's thrusting process."

Once this is learned, both are confident of the man's ability to withhold his orgasm. Anxiety is markedly reduced for both, and a normal length of intercourse is now possible.

In general, Semans and other investigators find fatigue and nervous strain are profound enemies of male control. Many examples are cited of men who are premature until the tension of a demanding job abates. Semans advises patients to sleep an hour or two before training sessions or before attempting intercourse. And, of course, the woman must be properly informed about her sexual role and physically able to fulfill it. For if she cannot be satisfied when intercourse is sustained for a reasonable length of time, the old anxiety and the feelings of inadequacy may again build male tension.

How long should a man be able to sustain intercourse without ejaculation? Obviously, the time varies with individuals and circumstances. With rapid friction, the time cannot be long for the average man. But in terms of establishing control, most doctors who treat prematurity feel success is reached when the man can sustain a coital connection for about five minutes. Dr. Popenoe reports that men treated for prematurity at the American Institute of Family Relations usually achieve at least ten minutes. And one authority, Dr. L. Aycock, finds questions of time are irrelevant once basic confidence and control are established; he feels that patients who can prolong intercourse for even a minute or two are able to last much longer.

These longer time periods reflect the feminine need for a slower, more studied and deliberate stimulation. But with a sexually aware woman, time periods beyond ten minutes are rarely needed.

When longer intercourse is possible, some women (Kinsey believes about 14 percent) discover that they experience not one but two or more orgasms before the male climax. While a single orgasm is satisfying for most women—and indeed an hour or more of rest is required before intercourse will again be effective —it is not necessarily satisfaction enough for the "multi-orgasmic woman." Some researchers suggest that the man ought, if he can, to attempt to hold back through the woman's orgasm on some occasion to learn if she is capable of being multi-orgasmic.

Ford and Beach report: "It is true that many women do not recognize their ability to achieve several climaxes in succession. This may be because they have never been stimulated for a sufficient length of time. A woman lacking premarital experience and married to a man whose orgasm occurs within one or two minutes after penetration might easily have one peak in her curve of responsiveness and then fail to have any subsequent ones simply because her partner's loss of erection removes the source of stimulation."

In this sense, the man with a multi-orgasmic wife might be thought premature if he controls himself only until she has experienced one climax. But evidently, a man who learns control can sometimes maintain it even through the vigorous thrusting and rapid friction of feminine orgasm.

Dr. Popenoe says: "The treatment of premature ejaculation has a real parallel in the treatment of sexual failure in women. First, a full understanding of what takes place physically in sexual activity is needed. Then the man must learn an *awareness* of his sexual function, just as the woman must. He must know control is possible for all men, just as coital orgasm is possible for all women. And he, like the unresponsive woman, must be relieved of tension and fearfulness, in order to cultivate his physical and emotional sensitivity to himself, to his partner and to the moment."

11

some practical questions

THE sexual information set out in these pages is yet incomplete. Tomorrow the knowledge of science will be fuller, to permit more certain answers to the sexual questions of men and women.

We have seen, however, that even our imperfect knowledge can rather quickly relieve the sexual failures of most marriages, that prompt help is now possible. The practical question is: How are the partners to get that help?

It is true that most of the researchers in the field are also doing clinical work, but usually on a very small scale. For example, USC's Kegel Clinic manages only a small handful of patients in a week, and even most of these are not simply sexual problems. Masters and Johnson provide a few couples with their two-week course of therapy. But at $2,500 for the course, it is beyond the means of most.

Few medical professionals are yet willing or able to undertake such cases. Psychiatrists—at $40 an hour and more—are too few even to handle the psychotics in our crowded mental wards. Gynecologists are swamped with tumors, infections and childbirths. Family doctors are so besieged by patients that most can spend only a fraction of the time recommended on physical examinations. And we have seen that few of these people have had much special training in sex problems.

Moreover, beyond the fact that few are able to give help on sexual problems, most of those who need the help are too anxious or ashamed to seek it. Sexual failure is not easy to talk about—especially when the patient suspects that he may be gently rebuffed or politely ignored, that he may have to confide in many before he finds a sympathetic ear linked to an informed mind. What then can a couple do about sexual failure?

First, let us remind ourselves that almost all couples have the potential for normal sexual performance. Once ignorance and some of its emotional handmaidens have been removed, Dr. Paul Popenoe points out, "the inherent mechanism of orgasm, which is certainly deeply ingrained in human nature by millions of years of evolution, can be expected to operate. . . . It may be *taken for granted* that the necessary sexual mechanism is not lacking."

Dr. Donald Hastings confirms in his review of what is known of feminine sexual response: "Most experts agree that every woman has the potential [for orgasm] whether she has ever experienced orgasm or not."

Thus, a woman may assume that she *can* respond. As for her husband, whose problem is generally the opposite—that of responding too quickly—Dr. John Oliven expresses the prevalent medical view when he writes: "It is dubious if a genuine 'inability to control emission' exists, except in very inexperienced young husbands."

If the potential for orgasm belongs to nearly all women, and the potential for control belongs to nearly all men, the next question is: Why does it fail to be realized? Few couples are likely to find the answers alone. For we have seen that sexual response is the sum of a bewildering array of physical, emotional and circumstantial factors. The subtlety—in fact, the virtual hopeless-ness—of accurately diagnosing the web which makes each in-dividual barrier is overwhelming. And we have seen that by the time the couple is aware of their need, the failure itself has added a complex overlay of fear and anger and doubt. Small wonder that most professionals, when confronted by this sad human jigsaw puzzle, have beaten a dignified retreat.

Modern sex research has not solved the problem. Instead, armed with the new physical knowledge, it has learned to circum-vent it. And in practical terms, herein lies the answer for most couples. Let us see how this approach operates.

First, there can be disorders, some of them serious, which prevent a satisfactory sex relationship. Certainly some sexual malfunctions are important symptoms of disease and should be investigated promptly. For women, these would include actual pain in intercourse, a sore on the genital organs which does not heal, persistent bleeding or discharge from the vagina or the urinary opening, regular bleeding after intercourse, or any true discomfort during sexual relations. A doctor should be consulted if any of these signs persists longer than two weeks.

For men, the warning signs are similar. They would include pain on erection of the penis; pain or discomfort during inter-course, ejaculation or urination; pain or discomfort in the peri-neal area (between the legs, behind the testicles); bleeding or discharge from the penis; any sore which does not heal.

Failure to become erect is, of course, also a signal to consult a physician. And urinary difficulties of any kind should send either men or women to the doctor, as should back pain or other discomfort which follows sexual relations regularly.

It is worthwhile for any woman who does not find sexual rela-tions satisfactory to see her doctor, preferably her gynecologist or obstetrician, if she has one. He may possibly find a physical problem, especially a weakness of the P.C. muscle. Since only a minority of doctors will ask a woman about the state of her sex life, she should not expect the doctor to guess her difficulty. She must take a deep breath and tell him what is wrong.

The man who suffers from impotence (failure to become erect) or premature ejaculation should not simply make an appointment for a checkup, hoping the doctor may notice something wrong. It is most unlikely that he will be able to determine the trouble unaided. The man must tell his doctor what has brought him. These sexual problems are quite unlikely to have anything to do with his physical maleness. Prematurity, especially, is characteristically male. Impotence is not usually, as some men fear, a sign of homosexuality—unless, for example, a man is potent with other males, but not with a woman.

Either a man or a woman seeking help should bear in mind that a sexually imperfect marriage is less the exception than the rule, and should not be ashamed of lack of sex information. Such a lack is also very definitely the rule. When researchers at the University of Virginia tested the levels of sex information among medical students, they found them extremely poor, and found that more than a few of the faculty were not much better informed.

If there are no physical abnormalities, the couple can certainly begin to make their own efforts to apply the information in this text. (Actually, nothing is suggested here which in itself can be harmful. The concern is rather that any sexual difficulty or discomfort which is actually a sign of disease might be neglected.)

A little conversation is certainly not amiss, for we have seen that some basic attitudes can be barriers or can enhance physical barriers—as the reluctance of many women to allow themselves to be women with sexual feelings and needs. The most important attitude, however, is a mutual will toward a fresh start, with an absence of blame, with as much rejection as possible of old resentments and an absolute suppression of old arguments about who is at fault. Each must give the other a chance to perform without demand or criticism. This is not a time to keep score, but one to practice and to learn, without anxiety about the outcome. The outcome will take care of itself.

As one expert comments: "One can almost compare the physiological process to learning to ride a bicycle. At first, it may seem hopeless. If the legs coordinate properly, balance is lost. If balance is kept, one cannot focus one's attention to steer. But because all the needed mechanisms are there, in an unbelievably short time they have formed themselves into a pattern. Balance, leg and arm motions all become automatic, a series of integrated reflexes which take over whenever one mounts a bicycle—until, if one has to teach another to ride, one has to think very hard to puzzle out just how it is done.

"We certainly would not dream of shouting at a child who has had no instruction, except to run from bicycles because they are dangerous, 'Damn it, why aren't you riding? Everyone else can do it. Are you trying to make me look like a bad parent?' Yet we do precisely this with intercourse, a far more subtle matter emotionally and physically.

"Make such demands on a child, and chances are the pressure will keep him from learning ever. He will probably hate bicycles and hate you. With sex, we tend to demand perfect performance at once and to blame the partner who fails, who blames the other in turn. The blame may be silent. But each knows what is in the other's mind."

More than an open attitude toward experiment and learning, without pressure to perform, the couple needs an attitude of cultivating and enjoying the pleasure of each moment, each detail of sensation, each perception of one's own body and of another's. This, coupled with the physical information we have reviewed, provides what may be the most important sexual principle of all. This is what Dr. Kegel describes as "awareness of function," an awareness of our physical role in sex which must gradually work its way into brain and nerve and muscle.

This, as has been explained, is one of the chief values of exercising the P.C. muscle. It enables a woman to find more than a physical perception. It allows her to participate as a woman, to seek the response of a mature woman by the consciously aware use of the organs which make her a woman.

These exercises, it should be stressed again, are not harmful. And even in the unusual woman whose muscle tone is well developed, they will teach a function and awareness which may not fully be hers. In more than a few cases, women with good muscle tone have been known to lack dependable sexual response, sometimes because of lack of awareness, and sometimes because of the sexual technique of the husband, who does not understand his wife's sexual role or her means of stimulation.

With good muscle tone on the part of the woman, with reasonable control on the part of the man, and with the techniques of intercourse we have discussed, the woman should feel sexual stimulation from the male organ in intercourse. Feeling this stimulation, she should be able to respond, if she is not under pressure.

But this pressure may exist deep in her psyche. And if this is the case, she needs some guidance. Old angers and resentments toward the wifely role might restrain her; her old attachments may hold her to adolescence. Such situations obtain in only a minority of women, and even in most of these cases, as we have explained, the barrier of anger or fear or love is not buried deep. Most of the time, it seems, physical understanding and technique can bypass such problems, and will. This accounts for the success of the new physical approaches to unresponsiveness. But in some women the barriers do not yield without some help.

This help need not be long-term psychiatric therapy. Probably the best solution for women whose unresponsiveness persists is a request that the family doctor furnish the name of a good marriage counselor. If the doctor does not have such a name, he can get recommendations from his local medical association. The important thing is to make certain that the counselor is qualified and able, for unhappily there are incompetents in the field.

Another reason for approaching a counselor through a physician is that your doctor might spot a more serious emotional disturbance of which sexual failure is a symptom. The same will be true of a well-trained professional marriage counselor. In either case, a referral to psychiatric help can be made. Such a referral, however, is unlikely to be necessary. In most cases, those who need psychiatric help seem to be aware that they need it. (True, there are disturbed people, particularly psychotics, who are unaware of their need for help. But even among the very seriously disturbed, the vast majority know there is something wrong, though they may deny it to others and resist the idea of treatment.)

Assuming what is likely to be the case—that physical information, understanding, and a new attitude toward sex are all that are needed to overcome most sexual failure—some practical questions still remain. Many of these center on the intensity and frequency of sexual need and response.

One of the most characteristic factors of sexual behavior is that it has infinite variety among different individuals and within the individual as well. As Dr. Philip Polatin comments: "We must bear in mind that all our sexual responses are highly dependent upon our emotional state. Fluctuation of desire and enjoyment must be expected in the happiest of marriages. If we maintain reasonable expectations of ourselves as well as our mates, we interpose fewer barriers to sexual enjoyment."

Kinsey reached the conclusion that there were intrinsic individual differences in sex behavior, especially in women, and much of the literature seems to confirm this idea, though as yet science has found no way to explain or measure these differences. Kinsey says: ". . . The exceedingly rapid responses of certain females who are able to reach orgasm within a matter of seconds . . . and the remarkable ability of some females to reach orgasm repeatedly within a short period of time, are capacities which most individuals could not conceivably acquire through training, childhood experience, or any sort of psychiatric therapy. Similarly, it seems reasonable to believe that at least some of the females who are slower in their responses are not equipped anatomically or physiologically in the same way as those who respond more rapidly."

The newer knowledge of sexual response can explain some of these differences, but not all of them. Some men and women want very frequent sexual activity; others want little. Some want repeated intercourse within a few hours or even a few minutes. For some men, however, any stimulation of the penis for some time after orgasm is actually quite painful.

This does not mean that a woman who has not responded sexually before will not change her feelings and her behavior, once she responds, and finds sex more satisfying. But by and large, most people are aware of their own sexual capacities and desires and change little in this regard.

There is probably one exception to the general rule of following one's own sexual propensities, and this applies to the marriage of many years. Dr. Popenoe says: "Most marriages, after ten, twenty or thirty years, would benefit by more frequent intercourse than actually occurs."

Dr. Popenoe explains that with the passing years we need even more reassurance of love and our physical attractiveness. He suggests that couples fall out of the habit of physical love, much to their loss. And he urges that they seek sexual arousal once or twice a week, with the woman especially being more aggressive and seductive. For menopause does not seem to affect sexual desire in women, and there seems to be no equivalent change in men.

It is worth noting that sex-organ changes in the middle years seem to be minor in terms of their effect on sexual function. In fact, some experts think sexual inactivity leads to a loss of sexual capacity. Though some of that capacity certainly fails in advanced years, sexual abilities appear to be sustained by use. As with many other physical capacities, we relinquish them too soon by neglect.

Certainly, we give up easily that which does not satisfy us, or which perhaps even stirs feelings of frustration, self-doubt and inadequacy. When these feelings derive from our attempts to express love, the wound is deep indeed. For what else is so essentially and characteristically human as our need to be loved and to give love?

"I've treated many thousands of cases," says Dr. Arnold Kegel. "And the one thing of which I am certain is that there is really no such thing as a cold woman, or a cold man. In their hearts, they are warm and loving. But the ability to express that warmth is locked away. We work to provide them with a key."

bibliography

Because this book is not intended primarily for a professional audience, it is not fully annotated. However, some of the authorities who reviewed the manuscript suggested that since this was the first time some of this material had been collated, technical readers might wish to consult the original sources.

For this reason, the following bibliographic plan has been chosen: First, when specific opinions or research are cited, the references are listed according to chapter except when stated in the text. Second, in support of what is here presented as current medical belief—especially in discussions of anatomy and physiology—a sampler is provided of the sources consulted, though without precise annotative reference as to page, etc. Because these latter texts provide material for more than one section of the book, they are listed in the bibliography of the chapter in which they are first applied.

CHAPTER 1

Dr. Popenoe's comment on information available is from:

1. Popenoe, P. *Marital Counselling with Special Reference to Frigidity.* American Institute of Family Relations Publication No. 502. Los Angeles.

Typical of older manuals still in wide use are:

2. Van de Velde, Th. *Ideal Marriage: Its Physiology and Technique.* New York: Random House, 1926.

3. Stopes, M. C. *Married Love.* New York: Eugenics Publishing Co., 1931.

4. Reik, T. *Psychology of Sex Relations.* New York: Reinhart, 1945.

5. Stone, H. M., and A. Stone. *A Marriage Manual.* New York: Simon and Schuster, 1953.

Ellis' remarks are from:

6. Ellis, H. *Sex and Marriage.* New York: Random House, 1952.

Similar views are also expressed in:

7. Ellis, H. *Studies in the Psychology of Sex.* New York: Random House, 1936.

CHAPTER 2

The cases cited here and elsewhere are based upon histories from the American Institute of Family Relations, though broadly adapted to protect privacy.

Quotations cited in this chapter are from personal interviews with those quoted, with their permission.

Dr. Hastings' comment is from:

8. Hastings, D. W. *A Doctor Speaks on Sexual Expression in Marriage.* Boston: Little, Brown, 1966.

CHAPTER 3

The definition of frigidity is from:

9. *Taber's Cyclopedic Medical Dictionary.* Philadelphia: F. A. Davis and Co., 1962.

The concept of frigidity as a neurotic symptom is expressed by Freud in a number of works. Typical is:

10. Freud, S. "Three Contributions to the Theory of Sex," *The Basic Writings of Sigmund Freud.* New York: Random House, 1938.

Dr. Robinson's opinions are from:

11. Robinson, M. N. *The Power of Sexual Surrender.* New York: Doubleday, 1959.

Stekel's categories of frigidity are stated in:

12. Stekel, W. *Frigidity in Woman.* New York: Boni and Liveright, 1926. Freud's letter is previously unpublished, and is from the personal collection of Dr. Arnold H. Kegel.

Stekel's speculations on sociologic and physical causes of frigidity are also found in 12.

Dickinson's studies are reported in:

13. Dickinson, R. L., and L. Beam. *A Thousand Marriages, a Medical Study of Sex Adjustment.* Baltimore: Williams and Wilkins Co., 1934.

Further of his studies are found in:

14. Dickinson, R. L., and L. Beam. *The Single Woman*. Baltimore: Williams and Wilkins Co., 1934.

15. Dickinson, R. L., and J. H. Pierson. "The Average Sex Life of American Women," *Journal of the American Medical Association*, 1925.

The three European studies are cited by Stekel in 12.

Landis' findings are from:

16. Ford, C. S., and F. A. Beach. *Patterns of Sexual Behavior*. New York: Harper and Brothers and Paul B. Hoeber, Inc., 1951.

The Air Force data are from:

17. Lowry, T. P. "Initial Coital Experiences: When and with Whom," *Military Medicine*, October 1964.

Ford and Beach make their prediction in 16.

Kinsey's figures are found in:

18. Kinsey, Pomeroy, Martin and Gebhard. *Sexual Behavior in the Human Female*. Philadelphia: W. B. Saunders Co., 1953.

The Wallin-Clark studies referred to in this chapter are from:

19. Wallin, P., and A. Clark. "A Study of Orgasm as a Condition of Women's Enjoyment of Coitus in the Middle Years of Marriage," *Human Biology*, May 1963.

20. Wallin, P. "A Study of Orgasm as a Condition of Women's Enjoyment of Intercourse," *Journal of Social Psychology*, February 1960.

Dr. Mead's comment is from:

21. Mead, B. T. "Sexual Problems," *Medical Times*. October 1962.

Dr. Rubins' conclusion is from:

22. Rubins, I. "Marital Sex Behavior," *Medical Times*, March 1964.

Dr. Corner's comment is from:

23. Lloyd, C. W. (ed.) *Introduction in Human Reproduction and Sexual Behavior*. Philadelphia: Lea and Febiger, 1964.

Dr. Lief summarizes his views on sex education in medical schools in:

24. "Sexual Disorder and Marriage," a chapter in *Marriage Counselling in Medical Practice*, a symposium. Chapel Hill: University of North Carolina Press, 1964.

Dr. Auerback's comment is from a University of California news release.

Dr. Golden's comment is from:

25. Golden, J. "Management of Sexual Problems by the Physician," *Obstetrics and Gynecology*, March 1964.

Dr. Brem's comment is from a personal interview.

CHAPTER 4

The sexual and reproductive physiology and anatomy are described from many sources, among which the following were most helpful:

26. Greenhill, J. P. *Office Gynecology*. Chicago: The Year Book Publishers, 1959.

27. Greenhill, J. P. *Obstetrics*. Philadelphia: W. B. Saunders Co., 1965.
28. Huffman, J. W. *Gynecology and Obstetrics*. Philadelphia: W. B. Saunders Co., 1962.
29. Novak, E. R., Jones and Jones. *Novak's Textbook of Gynecology*. Baltimore: The Williams and Wilkins Co., 1965.
30. Francis, C. C. *Introduction to Human Anatomy*. St. Louis: C. V. Mosby Co., 1964.
31. Campbell, M. F. *Urology*. Philadelphia: W. B. Saunders Co., 1963.
32. Hamm, F. C. *Urology in Medical Practice*. Philadelphia: J. B. Lippincott, 1962.
33. Smith, D. R. *General Urology*. Los Altos: Lange Medical Publications, 1963.

Publications of Masters which were used include:

34. Masters, W. H., and V. E. Johnson. "The Sexual Response of the Human Male," *Western Journal of Surgery, Obstetrics and Gynecology*, March 1963.
35. Masters, W. H., and V. E. Johnson. "The Sexual Response Cycle of the Human Female, I," *Western Journal of Surgery. Obstetrics and Gynecology*, 1960.
36. Masters, W. H., and V. E. Johnson. "The Sexual Response Cycle of the Human Female, II," *Annals of the New York Academy of Medicine*, 1959.
37. Masters, W. H., and V. E. Johnson. "The Human Female," *Anatomy of Sexual Response*. Minnesota Medicine, 1960.
38. Masters, W. H., and V. E. Johnson. Chapter in *Encyclopedia of Sexual Behavior*. New York: Hawthorn, 1961.
39. Masters, W. H., and V. E. Johnson. "The Artificial Vagina: Anatomic. Physiologic, Psychosexual Function," *Western Journal of Surgery, Obstetrics and Gynecology*, 1961.
40. Masters, W. H., and V. E. Johnson. *Human Sexual Response*. Boston: Little, Brown, 1966.
41. Guze, H. "Anatomy and Physiology of Sex," *Encyclopedia of Sexual Behavior*, Vol. I. New York: Hawthorn, 1961.

The Baruck-Miller comment is from:

42. Baruck, D. W., and H. Miller. *Sex and Marriage: New Understandings*. New York: Harper and Brothers, 1962.

Dr. Huffman's research is reported in:

43. Huffman, J. W. "The Effect of Gynecologic Surgery on Sexual Reactions," *American Journal of Obstetrics and Gynecology*, April 1950.

Freud's view of sexual-response development is seen in:

44. Freud, S. "The Transformation of Puberty," *The Basic Writings of Sigmund Freud*. New York: Random House, 1938.

For Ford and Beach's conclusions, see 16.

For Dr. Robinson's comment, see 11.

Dr. Popenoe's statement is from a personal interview.

Dr. Polatin's remarks are from:

45. Polatin, P., and E. Philtine. *Marriage in the Modern World*. Philadelphia: J. P. Lippincott, 1961.

CHAPTER 5

References dealing with anatomy and physiology in this chapter include those listed above for Chapter 4.

Dr. Kegel's work is described in some of the following sources:

46. Kegel, A. H. "Non-Surgical Treatment of Genital Relaxation," *Annals of Western Medicine and Surgery*, May 1948.

47. Kegel, A. H. "Progressive Resistance Exercise in the Functional Restoration of the Perineal Muscles," *American Journal of Obstetrics and Gynecology*, August 1948.

49. Kegel, A. H. "The Physiologic Treatment of Poor Tone and Function of the Genital Muscles and of Urinary Stress Incontinence," *Western Journal of Surgery, Obstetrics and Gynecology*, November 1949.

50. Kegel, A. H. "Physiologic Therapy of Urinary Stress Incontinence," *Journal of the American Medical Association*, July 7, 1951.

51. Kegel, A. H. "Stress Incontinence and Genital Relaxation," *Ciba Symposium*, February-March, 1952.

52. Kegel, A. H. "Sexual Functions of the Pubococcygeus Muscle," *Western Journal of Surgery, Obstetrics and Gynecology*, 1952.

53. Kegel, A. H. "Active Exercise of the Pubococcygeus Muscle," Meigs and Sturgis (eds.), in *Progress in Gynecology*. New York: Grune and Stratton, 1950.

54. Kegel, A. H., and T. O. Powell. "The Physiologic Treatment of Urinary Stress Incontinence," *Journal of Urology*, May 1950.

55. Kegel, A. H. "Office Treatment of Genital Prolapse," *Current Medical Digest*, July 1953.

56. Kegel, A. H. "Stress Incontinence of Urine in Women; Physiologic Treatment," *Journal of the International College of Surgeons*, April 1965.

57. Kegel, A. H. Chapter in J. P. Greenhill (ed.), *The Year Book of Obstetrics and Gynecology*. Chicago: The Year Book Publishers, 1965.

See also:

58. Yousseff, A. F. Chapter 20 in *Gynecological Urology*. Springfield: Charles C. Thomas, 1960.

McGuire and Steinhilber's comments are from:

59. McGuire, T. F., and R. M. Steinhilber. "Sexual Frigidity," *Mayo Clinic Proceedings*, June 1964.

For Dr. Dickinson's observations, see 13.

For Dr. Hastings' comment, see 8.

Dr. Oliven's comments are from:

60.   Oliven, J. F. *Sexual Hygiene and Pathology, A Manual for the Physician and the Professions.* Montreal: J. P. Lippincott, 1965.

CHAPTER 6

Dickinson's interest in the pelvic floor muscles is from 13 and:

61.   Dickinson, R. L. *Atlas of Human Sex Anatomy.* Baltimore: Williams and Wilkins Co., 1949.

For Van de Velde's view, see 2.

Dr. Hungerford's comments are from a personal interview.

For Lloyd's comment, see his chapter in 23.

For Oliven's statements in this chapter, see 60.

Benson's opinions on stress incontinence are stated in:

62.   Benson, R. C. *Handbook of Obstetrics and Gynecology.* Los Altos: Lange Medical Publications, 1964. His other comments which are used here are from the same text, which also served in other questions as typical of the opinion of modern gynecology and obstetrics.

CHAPTER 7

A good summary of early Indian love manuals may be found in one edition of the *Koka Shastra*, in which Archer provides samplings from each major text, from the *Kamasutra* onward.

63.   Kokkoka, *Koka Shastra* (translation, introduction, notes by A. Comfort; preface by W. G. Archer). New York: Ballantine Books, 1966 or Stein and Day, 1965.

The anthropological data are largely from 16.

On the stimulative uses of foods:

64.   Deutsch, R. M. *The Nuts among the Berries.* New York: Ballantine Books, 1961.

The data on time differences in orgasm are from 18 and 65.

65.   Kinsey, Pomeroy and Martin. *Sexual Behavior in the Human Male.* London and Philadelphia: W. B. Saunders Co., 1948.

For quotations from Kinsey, see 18.

For a summary of Masters' views of the functional role of the vagina in coitus, see 40. Kegel's views were first outlined in 52; however, these are now amplified by yet-unpublished research, some of which Kegel reported on in 1968 at a University of Southern California School of Medicine symposium on sexual problems.

Dr. Popenoe's statement on vaginal sensations is from:

66.   Popenoe, P. *Sex, Love and Marriage.* New York: Belmont Books, 1963.

CHAPTER 8

Masters' statement was made at the annual 1968 meeting of the American Fertility Society in San Francisco.

A paper on the success of rapid treatment of sex problems at the American Institute of Family Relations is in preparation by a consulting physician (K. Morgan).

Dr. Kaplan is quoted in:

67. "The $2500 Understanding," *Newsweek*, June 1968.

For the Ford and Beach quotation, see 16.

Mrs. Johnson's quotation is made in a paper delivered by her at the American Fertility Society meeting noted above.

Pearl Buck's comments are from:

68. Cassarra, B. (ed.). *American Women: The Changing Image*. Boston: Beacon, 1962.

For Dr. Mead's comment, see 68.

Labor statistics and economic figures are from material distributed by the Office of Economic Opportunity, by the Department of Labor, and by the Treasury Department. See also:

69. "Women's Role," *U.S. News and World Report*, May 30, 1966.

70. "When Mothers Work," *Newsweek*, August 28, 1967.

CHAPTER 9

For McGuire and Steinhilber's statements, see 59.

For Havelock Ellis' statement, see his introduction in 13.

The case material used here is based upon interviews with counselors at the American Institute of Family Relations and other professionals.

CHAPTER 10

Dr. Damrau's conclusion and other citations from his work are in:

71. Damrau, F. "Use of Ethyl Amino Benzoate to Prolong Coitus," *Journal of Urology*, June 1963.

Masters' comment on prematurity is from a paper delivered at the 1968 meeting of the American Fertility Society.

For Lloyd's comment, see 23.

Modern thinking about premature ejaculation is also summarized in the following:

72. Aycock, L. "The Medical Management of Premature Ejaculation," *Journal of Urology*, September 1949.

73. Wershub, L. P. *Sexual Impotence in the Male*. Philadelphia: Charles Thomas, 1959.

74. Podolsky, E. "Therapeutic Measures in Sexual Impotence," *Medical Digest*, June 1956.

75. Johnson, R. H. "Premature Ejaculation." Unpublished guidance paper for the staff of the American Institute of Family Relations, Los Angeles.
The California study is explained in 1.
Schapiro's summary is from:

76. Schapiro, B. "Premature Ejaculation: A Review of 1130 Cases," *Journal of Urology*, 1943.
See also:

77. Schapiro, B. "Potency Disorders in the Male, a Review of 1960 Cases of Premature Ejaculation." Harefuah, 1953.
Semans reports his methods in:

78. Semans, J. H. "Premature Ejaculation: A New Approach," *Southern Medical Journal*, 1956.
Masters has published no report of this approach at this writing, though he recounted it at the 1968 American Fertility Society meeting.
For Kinsey's statements on multiple orgasm, see 18.
For the statement by Ford and Beach, see 16.
Dr. Popenoe's comment is from a personal interview.

CHAPTER 11

For Dr. Popenoe's quotation, see 1.
For Dr. Hastings' quotation, see 8.
For Dr. Oliven's comment, see 60.
For Dr. Polatin's opinion, see 45.
For Kinsey's conclusion, see 18.
Dr. Popenoe's comment on intercourse in later marriage is from:

79. Popenoe, P. "Sex after 40," a paper privately printed by the American Institute of Family Relations for distribution among patients.
Dr. Kegel's statement is from a personal interview.

RONALD M. DEUTSCH is among the nation's foremost popular writers on medicine. As a regular contributor to the *Reader's Digest* and as a frequent contributor of articles on health problems to magazines such as the *Ladies' Home Journal*, *Redbook* and *Family Circle* and a score of others, Mr. Deutsch's shorter works now number well over two hundred. This broad experience in health education has brought him invitations to present papers at many scientific meetings, ranging from the National Congress on Medical Quackery to conferences of the National Society for the Prevention of Blindness, where physicians and other health professionals have sought his aid in the conveying of health information to the public. His study of nutrition frauds and fallacies is widely used as a text. Reprints of his articles have been distributed by the hundreds of thousands from voluntary health agencies such as the American Cancer Society, the American Heart Association, and the American Diabetes Association. Particularly, he is noted for his effective presentation of little-known health problems to the public, and of problems which many feared could not be tastefully conveyed to mass audiences. His concern with the hidden and the neglected in health led almost inevitably to this effort to expunge the sexual ignorance which is almost universal in American marriages, and to spell out the little-known sex research of recent decades.